Island
of Wildlife

*The story of Fingringhoe Wick -
a gravel pit nature reserve*

by Laurie Forsyth

THE *wildlife* TRUSTS

ESSEX
Wildlife Trust

Contents

Foreword by Chris Gibson   *iv*
Introduction   1

Chapter
1   Island of wildlife   3
2   Outpost of Rome to industrial wasteland   10
3   The creation of a nature reserve: 1961–1964   18
4   Natural succession: The big greening   25
5   Living at The Wick   31
6   Walking with nightingales   36
7   A maturing landscape: 1975–1979   39
8   Winners and losers   44
9   Brent goose odyssey   48
10   Forty years of wildlife conservation   51
    Memory Lane   56

Wildlife reports   58
    Mammals   59
    Birds   61
    Reptiles and amphibians   64
    The ponds and their aquatic invertebrates   65
    Molluscs: Snails and slugs   67
    Arachnida: Pseudo-scorpions, harvestmen
         and spiders   69
    Coleoptera: Beetles   72
    Galls   75
    Heteroptera: Plant bugs   77
    Hymenoptera: Bees, wasps and ants   79
    Lepidoptera: Moths and butterflies   82
    Odonata: Dragonflies and damselflies   86
    Orthoptera: Crickets and grasshoppers   89
    Flora   91
    Bryophyta: Mosses and liverworts   94
    Fungi   96
    Lichens   98

Appendix
    Species list of flora and fauna recorded in
    the nature reserve 1961–2004   101

Foreword

'You must go to Fingringhoe Wick, and meet Laurie Forsyth'. Some of the first words of my then senior officer Robin Hamilton when I joined the Nature Conservancy Council in 1985. Both were quite unknown to me at the time, but the natural riches of 'The Wick' soon became familiar as I explored my new haunts. I watched brent geese on the Colne Estuary, which has the reserve at its heart, and then a few months later lost myself in the glorious soundscape of nightingales welcoming the summer – an early taste of what it had to offer.

But much more was to come as I got to know Laurie. I realised at once he was a kindred spirit – a naturalist, conservationist and enthusiast for wildlife, but one who has vision and is prepared to make that vision a reality. So began a long and fruitful partnership. Once the euphoria of my discovery of this gem of a site subsided, it was clear to me that it could be so much better. The problem – trees and scrub, too many in the wrong places, squeezing the lifeblood out of the heaths, and restricting the special insects and plants to isolated favourable pockets. The answer – to understand the essential dynamics of the site, to recognise that natural succession over the previous 40 years was resulting in its rich mosaic of habitats becoming swamped and homogenised under a blanket of growth.

A familiar story. Management was taking place, but only scratching the surface. And fortunately Laurie felt the same. He had seen the changes occurring, but more importantly realised what could be achieved in terms of setting back the ecological clock, using the fruits of modern technology. Bulldozers and excavators, so often the agents of destruction, could be brought in to restore that which was being lost. At times, it looked like a building site. It was: building biodiversity! Laurie had the vision, and found the ways to deliver, and The Wick can now look forward to a diverse future with confidence.

That it is, and looks set to remain, one of the Trust's flagship reserves, as is demonstrated so clearly in this book, is testament to the work of the Trust and especially to the vision, commitment and perseverance of Laurie Forsyth. It is especially fitting that this celebration of the riches of The Wick is published to coincide with his retirement. He will be a hard act to follow, but the state he has left it in, with an eye to the future as well as a nod to the past, gives me confidence that Fingringhoe Wick will still serve to delight us all for many years to come.

Dr Chris Gibson

Senior Conservation Officer,
English Nature, Colchester

Introduction

You could walk past it and never give it a glance. In fact, viewers in the Lake bird hides at Fingringhoe Wick nature reserve see it every day. The Mound is directly opposite the hides, on the other side of the lake. About 7 m long, and 3 m high, it's not a mountain. To me though, it is perhaps the most interesting and thought-stimulating feature of 'The Wick'. It is made of loess, a finely powdered silt blown here by strong winds at a time when much of Essex was freezing, arid tundra. In their search for sand and ballast, the operators of the gravel pit ignored The Mound, and so its summit still indicates the level of the 19th-century farm that preceded the gravel pit. Standing beneath The Mound, it is fun to imagine the cattle and sheep that once grazed the invisible pasture way above your head.

Two thousand years earlier a Romano-British family farmed the same land. He may have been a retired veteran of the army of Rome: she was probably a local Trinovantes girl. The disposal of their household rubbish was simple and effective, and one of their many midden ditches lies concealed in The Mound. The ditch is packed with all sorts of Roman rubbish, especially oyster shells which have leached their calcium into the soil. Bee orchids grow at the foot of The Mound in the calcium-rich soil, and in summer solitary bees by the hundred buzz along the face and tunnel into its surface. Green woodpeckers chisel into the tough loess, and a fox likes to sleep on the sunny summit. The Mound is a living museum of geological, archaeological and natural history. There is a strong feeling of human and wildlife connections, where all strands are linked from an ancient ice age to the present Fingringhoe Wick nature reserve.

Known to its friends simply as 'The Wick', the reserve was created in 1961 when Essex Naturalists' Trust bought a 50-hectare industrial wasteland. Generations of wildlife have flourished at The Wick in my time. With the support of the Trust (now known as Essex Wildlife Trust), English Nature and the Heritage Lottery Fund, most of my plans have actually come into being, and the nature reserve in 2005 is in great shape. Almost from the first day, when my family moved into the warden's house, I have been blessed by the support of a small nucleus of volunteers – you know who you are – and I am thankful and a little stunned that they still support the wildlife, the nature reserve and me 26 years later. Literally hundreds of other volunteers pass un-named through these pages. Essex Wildlife Trust and past wardens of The Wick owe them, and their present-day successors a great deal. We couldn't have done it without them.

We moved into the warden's house in March 1979. It was raining. The

Wick Farm is the warden's house. *Photograph: Laurie Forsyth.*
All photographs in this book are by the author, except where others are named.

windows in the porch had to be taken out so that we could get the sofa into the house, and the electric kettle fused with a loud bang when my wife, Gina, tried to make a cup of tea. In short, it was a normal moving-in experience. Through sheets of driving rain the removals men peered into the murk and thought they had come to the very edge of civilisation.

Next morning was still and overcast. Early spring had come to The Wick, and wrens and chaffinches sang in the thickets. Looking back, I vividly recall the emotional experience of walking about the reserve for the first time as the warden. It was hard to believe that we were now to live in this wonderful place, and difficult not to suspect that fate was at work from the moment I had joined Stewart Linsell's working party six years earlier. I had a great feeling of elation at having escaped a grey future as a London commuter. Above all, a voice in my head kept shouting 'this is yours!' 26 years later, the voice is stronger than ever.

Laurie Forsyth

Fingringhoe Wick, May 2005

Chapter 1
Island of wildlife

Imagine you are a gull circling high above the Colne estuary. Far below, you can see Fingringhoe Wick as a small finger of roughness in a smooth, intensively farmed landscape. From up here, you can see how it acts as an island for wildlife in a wide sea of agriculture, where even in this relatively unpressured slice of Essex birds, animals and wild flowers are just a token of what they were 50 years ago. The vista underlines the importance of nature reserves, but emphasises even more the downward spiral of the quality of our countryside, and the importance of the ceaseless role Essex Wildlife Trust must play just to slow the decline. Climate change, rising sea levels, GM foods and North Sea wind farms, a planned expansion at Stansted and a huge surge of new housing development are all additional threats to wildlife, and our Trust needs to flourish and succeed as never before. Islands of wildlife – even though the Trust now has over 80 – weaken in time and fail through their isolation.

If Fingringhoe Wick were located near Braintree or Rochford it would still be a fine nature reserve. To most visitors however, it is the setting that puts The Wick in a class of its own. The estuary of the Colne dominates the reserve with its mudflats and salt marshes, and the smell of mud and seaweed puts a spring in the step of birdwatchers hurrying down to the Geedon Bay hide to see what is feeding out on the mud. It is November: thick mist hides the horizon to the south, and the Geedon salt marsh rolls away into apparent infinity. It looks how I imagine tundra looks: endless, flat, waterlogged and windswept. No wonder the Siberian brent geese feel at home here. Invisible curlew and grey plover call from the mudflats where they are feeding at the edge of the incoming tide. How different it is in May. With the North Sea glittering on the horizon, the estuary is sunny and full of activity. Sails skip across the waves, shelduck hurtle downwind, oystercatchers pipe in the distance, and wavelets slap the sand near the jetty.

Halfway along the reserve road to the Visitor Centre, visitors suddenly see the huge estuary spread before them. For first-timers, it is an exciting moment and a promise of good things to come. For veterans it is like seeing an old friend again. To me, and other staff, it is our 'wow' factor that we know will bring visitors back to The Wick again and again. Down through the centuries, the Colne and its estuary has influenced Fingringhoe Wick, its people and its wildlife, and always will.

If you are about to visit Fingringhoe

Herds of woolly mammoth and other now extinct ice age herbivores once migrated from the south each spring to feeding grounds on the Essex tundra. *Courtesy English Nature*.

Wick for the first time, you will find us on the west bank of the Colne, about four miles from Colchester. Having passed through Fingringhoe, drivers approach the nature reserve down narrow lanes that build a sense of anticipation, or possibly despair. Their first glimpse of the marshes and glittering river makes it all worthwhile. Passing through woodland and spinneys on the road to the Visitor Centre, new visitors are quite unaware that less than 100 years ago this was Wick Farm, a tranquil sheep and arable farm that had dozed for centuries on the banks of the Colne.

Hard times fell in the 1920s. With the knowledge that what lay beneath the ground was of greater value than the farm itself, Wick Farm was broken up and sold. Fifty hectares were bought by a gravel extractor, and took on a new life as the Freshwater Pit. Following four decades of upheaval that reduced that slice of Wick Farm to an industrial wasteland, the worked-out pit was closed down in 1959. With the *'For Sale'* signs up, the ex-farm and ex-pit was poised for another chameleon-like change in its fortunes. At that time, gravel extractors were not obliged to invest in the restoration of the landscape following gravel quarrying. Finding someone willing to buy a hole in the ground was not easy, however.

Essex Naturalists' Trust was founded in 1959 – the year the old pit closed. Under inspired leadership from its renowned founder members, within two years the embryonic Trust bought the old gravel workings. It was the first nature reserve we actually owned. For a small charity with tiny funds the purchase was far more difficult than this account suggests. The marriage was perfect: a vigorous, thrusting young organisation with a lot to prove but with scant resources, and a moonscape of a site with little attraction to other buyers, with tremendous wildlife potential, in a location of great scientific interest and scenic beauty. The Trust purchased the old pit for less than £4000 – a vast sum for us at the time. Fingringhoe Wick and its wildlife has flourished ever since. It is interesting to reflect that it would not exist at all if climatic events in the far distant past had been different.

Ice-cold Fingringhoe: Back to the beginning

Water runs downhill. Rivers flow to the sea. Nothing, not even the passing of half a million years changes the basic laws. We are locked into the timescale of our tiny human lives and find it almost impossible to grasp that Britain was once submerged beneath the ocean, or that vast volcanoes once erupted in the west. Given time, almost everything in the geological repertoire that can happen, has happened to the British Isles, from searing desert to frigid ice sheet. At a time when sea levels were low and we were joined by a land bridge to the continent, the river we call the Thames rose in the ancient Welsh mountains, and flowed eastwards across England. Passing close to Harlow, Chelmsford and Colchester, it was joined near Clacton by the north-flowing Medway, and then crossed the dry North Sea plain to join the immense river Rhine as one

of many tributaries. In a prolonged period of global cooling with glacier and ice sheet formation, sea level was about 100 m lower than at present.

Rivers wander about the landscape, forming new channels at times of flood. Over a period of many thousands of years, wide flood plains, criss-crossed with numerous channels and terraces are created where vast amounts of silt and gravel have been dropped by flood waters. At our present Essex coast, the gravel deposits are known as East Essex Gravels, and they underlie The Wick and most of north-east Essex. With global temperatures continuing to fall, the Earth entered another ice age. Taking thousands of years to develop, this ice age – the Anglian – was one of the most severe global coolings the planet has experienced. Lasting about 50,000 years, the continuous ice sheet that began life in the mountains of Scandinavia crunched across the dry plain and buried most of the British Isles in glittering ice 1 km thick. The early river Thames was blocked by the ice, and then diverted southwards towards its present course.

The Anglian ice sheet never covered the Essex coast. Lobes of ice reached Hornchurch, Brentwood and Chigwell, but the gravel ridge extending from Danbury to Tiptree probably marks its eastern edge. The ice sheet was lifeless. The climate was intensely cold and dry, and in winter the tundra that extended from the edge of the ice sheet was almost as hostile to life as the ice itself. In summer as the frozen ground thawed, grasses and sedges flowered in the waterlogged soil, and life became possible for a short time. Fossils indicate that Norway lemming, various voles, wild horse, red deer and reindeer lived on the summer tundra. Global temperatures at last began to rise, the ice sheet halted, and then slowly retreated to reveal a pulverised landscape. In the succeeding, much warmer, interglacial period, vegetation and wildlife colonised Britain from the continent; sea levels rose, and the continental land bridge was submerged.

But that is not the end of the story. Again the ice returned, and once again life was almost eliminated. The Devensian Ice Age – the most recent glaciation – lasted about 100,000 years and reached its peak 20,000 years ago. Although less severe than the Anglian Ice Age, the Devensian produced Arctic sea temperatures at the latitude of Lisbon. Once again, the climate see-saw swung, temperatures began to rise, and 14,000 years ago Britain was largely free of ice again. The retreating, decaying ice sheet released unimaginable torrents of melt water. Bearing all the shattered material scraped up and pulverised by the ice in its grinding progress across the land, the water transported and spread deposits of silt, sand and gravel far and wide, burying most of the older gravels dating from the Anglian Ice Age. There is a cliff in the working pit next to The Wick, where I have often gazed at the seams of gravel and sand laid down so long ago. In 1994 a dragline bucket exposed the deep cleft of a fossil ice wedge – the unmistakeable signature of a glacial climate.

In the warming climate of our present interglacial period, tundra in East Anglia gave way to successive waves of colonisation by plants from the continent, and woodland developed of birch, then pine, alder and hazel. Fossils reveal that reindeer, moose, wild horse, brown bear, lynx, wolverine, woolly mammoth and other large mammals crossed the land bridge. The herds were followed by man, the hunter.

Autumn 1981: With the leaves tumbling, suddenly I can see into thickets that a few weeks earlier were impenetrable walls of green. New, unexplored places beckon that just might conceal something special; a new fern, an unrecorded moss or even an unsuspected badger sett. Often there is nothing new. Today, I stare in disbelief at a large, perfectly chipped handaxe from the Palaeolithic – the Old Stone Age. It is made from an orange flint and lying on a heap of other flints as though the hunter had just placed it there whilst he tossed a log on the fire.

Colchester Castle Museum date the tool to anything from between 15,000 to 50,000 years ago. Was the hunter one of a group following the herds as the last ice age drew to a close? The ancient stone tool made a powerful connection between myself and a fur-clad hunter who survived by his instincts, with a knowledge of wildlife that I envy.

Left: Socketed late Bronze Age axe: 950–650 BC.
Above: Palaeolithic flint axe: from about 40,000 BC.
Courtesy Colchester Castle Museum.

Thames and Colne Aggregates began quarrying for gravel in land adjacent to The Wick many years ago. Since then, several examples of flint tools have come up the ramp and been rescued from crushing. These however are more recent, and date from about 4000 years ago. The finely shaped and polished flint handaxes are from the Neolithic – the New Stone Age – and they bear little resemblance to the roughly chipped handaxe I found. More impressive still are finely flaked flint spear points that are thin and almost translucent. These people were our first farmers, and to farm they needed open land. People capable of skilled flint work and growing crops and looking after livestock were also capable of the clearance of woodland. Forest which knew only the effects of storms, natural fire and grazing by wild animals was nibbled at for centuries by men wielding those polished flint axes, and later systematically burned. The Neolithic

farmers created and expanded the open land they needed, until the mystical, primeval wildwood we have heard so much about was eventually reduced to just isolated fragments. What was it actually like? We can only guess by observing ancient forests which still survive here and there on the continent. The ever-shrinking forest and the spread of people and their agriculture and livestock would eventually bring about the extinction of the brown bear, lynx, wolf and other large mammals that climbed aboard the ark before Britain became an island. Fossils prove that beaver, wild cattle, wild boar, pine marten, badger, fox, red deer, roe deer, otter and wild cat also flourished in the wildwood. It took about 3000 years to change a mainly forested land into one that was mainly farmed.

The decline in forest coverage and the wildlife it supported was counterbalanced by the incidental creation of grassland, scrub,

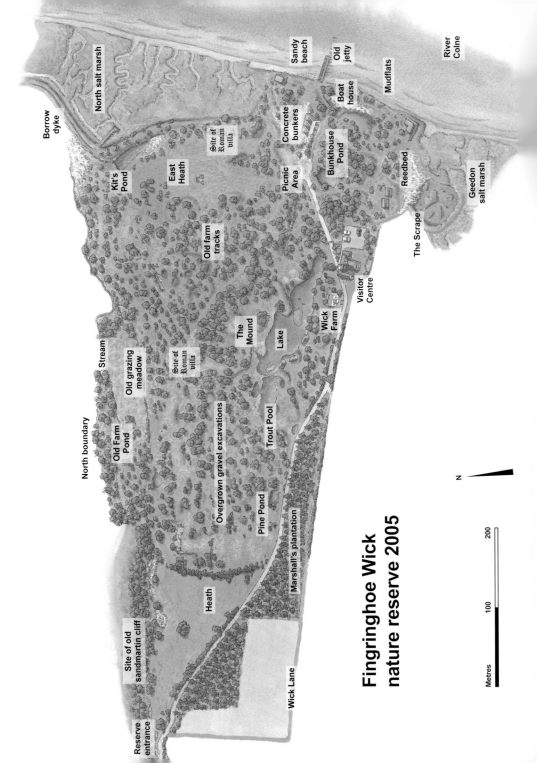

Fingringhoe Wick
nature reserve 2005

River Colne

Mudflats

Sandy beach

Old jetty

Boat house

North salt marsh

Borrow dyke

Concrete bunkers

Reedbed

Geedon salt marsh

The Scrape

Site of Roman villa

East Heath

Kit's Pond

Picnic Area

Bunkhouse Pond

Old farm tracks

Stream

Old grazing meadow

Site of Roman villa

The Mound

Lake

Visitor Centre

Wick Farm

North boundary

Old Farm Pond

Overgrown gravel excavations

Trout Pool

Pine Pond

Heath

Marshall's plantation

Site of old sandmartin cliff

Wick Lane

Reserve entrance

N

Metres 100 200

The Mound is a layer cake of human and natural history. and a reminder of a past ice age.

heathland, moorland, downland, ploughed fields, disturbed ground and other non-woodland habitats that owed their existence to regular activity by farmers. Birds, plants and insects in particular would have benefited from the increased range of habitats available to them, and, as the centuries passed, these new features became traditional in the farmed countryside, and vital to wildlife. They were indispensable to the farmer, and enabled him to grow crops and also to keep cattle, sheep and other domestic livestock.

Chapter 2

Outpost of Rome to industrial wasteland

The small bronze spoon lay winking in the first sunlight to strike it for 2000 years. It was perfect, and had clearly been accidentally thrown into the midden ditch with food scraps. The ditch is close to the jetty, and contains the usual fascinating household refuse found in all Roman middens at The Wick: lots of oystershells, a few cockles and mussels, broken pottery, fragments of tile, charcoal and ash from the fire, and sheep and cattle bones. Although I once found a small broken sickle, it is rare to find metal as it corrodes in the ground, and in any case was valuable and was usually recycled. One of the most evocative finds was a metal cooking pot of the type issued to Roman army legionaries. I have never ever found glass, and I presume that also was recycled.

Archaeologists became aware of Romano-British farm villas at The Wick in 1928, when large-scale gravel extraction commenced and bulldozers exposed characteristic material. Many artefacts were collected by the Revd G.M. Benton, by whose bequest they passed to Colchester Castle Museum. It contained many coins of the Claudian period. There were small metal items of military equipment, including a cavalry horse brass, and a series of fine brooches of Claudian date, a strigil, cow bells

and three small glass cups. A second building was discovered near Wick Farm, the warden's house, in 1936. Although it possessed a hypocaust, it appeared to be rather shoddily built, using materials recycled from another, more opulent building that was never discovered. The midden ditches associated with this building run beneath the garden of Wick Farm. Feeling the garden needed a pond, Paddy Lunt, a popular warden at The Wick in the late 1960s, started to dig. Soon, he was surrounded by oystershells and other Roman household debris which included large fragments of a wine or water flagon. The pond forgotten, Paddy collected the pieces and almost completely reassembled the ancient pot.

Gwen Foott, as a founder member of the Trust spent a lot of time at The Wick – often with her eyes fixed firmly on the ground. One day she found a perfect spoon carved from bone on the side of an eroding spoil heap. It appears the Romano-British were careless with their spoons. However, their loss is definitely our gain and the spoon was presented to Colchester Museum, as were all the other artefacts found over the years. The garden midden is exposed in a small cliff face above the lake. I have spent happy hours fossicking amongst cows' ribs, the jaw bones of sheep and pigs, oystershells and broken pottery. It's all rubbish – but it's Roman rubbish. The red gloss pottery known as Samian ware was widely produced in the Roman province of Gaul, and imported into Britannica. Each manufacturer placed his individual stamp on his work. As I write, a piece of Samian ware lies on the desk, clearly stamped with the name Asiaticus. Occasionally, to assist our management, we bring back to The Wick the sort of heavy earth-moving machinery that helped shape the original gravel pit landscape, and this can expose more artefacts.

I have only once found a coin. It lay in the bottom of a trench just excavated as part of a lakeside cliff to attract nesting kingfishers. The coin – the size of an old penny – was identified as a Roman *sestertius* issued by the emperor Trajan. Today, it would be worth about 50p in the shops. My son Jonathan Forsyth has a keen eye. In 2000, he spotted a small, corroded metal object on a spoil heap. Expertly cleaned and preserved by the museum, it was identified as a copper-alloy model of a ram. It was a votive figure: something given in fulfilment of a vow. In the same year he found a 'first', not just for The Wick, but for Britain. It was a tiny coin made by the Ambiani, a Celtic tribe living in north-east France at the time Gaul was conquered by Julius Caesar. With a typically stylistic Celtic swan on one

Paddy Lunt found the fragments of this Roman flagon when digging the garden pond seen in the background.

side, and a horse on the other, the coin is thought to have been brought to Britannica by a legionary in the invading Roman army in AD 43.

Rome valued the newest addition to her empire for the mineral wealth in the ground, the timber, and the suitability of the climate for arable crops that could be exported back home. Analysis of midden charcoal indicates that Roman coppice supported a similar variety of trees to the present. Other remains indicate that birds such as the spoonbill and crane lived in nearby marshes. It is thought that much of south-east England grew various arable crops, and east Essex was as suitable then as it is now for their production. The brown hare would have flourished in the farm fields, and native red deer and roe deer grazed in the woodlands. Ships exporting Essex grain to feed the empire accidentally introduced the black rat and the house mouse.

Medieval Fingringhoe: The heyday of Wick Farm

Nothing is known of Fingringhoe after the departure of the Roman legions. Emerging from the Dark Ages centuries later however, in AD 975 there is a Saxon reference to *Fingringaho,* which incorporates elements from Saxon and Norse, and is thought to refer to 'dwellers on the cleared spur of marshland'. In the 11th century, the Manor of Fingringhoe was included in the lands of the Priory of West Mersea. In 1046 Edward the Confessor granted the Priory to the Abbey of St Ouen, at Rouen in France. The manor of Fingringhoe was then leased to William, Bishop of London in 1202. The Priory and all its lands reverted to Henry V in 1414, following an Act of Parliament which dissolved all alien priories.

From Tudor times to the present

In 1553 Edward VI granted the manor to Thomas, Lord Darcy. It changed hands several times before passing to Joseph Keeling in 1751. He commissioned a survey of all the lands belonging to Fingringhoe Hall – his home. The survey was the source of the earliest known map of the site we call Fingringhoe Wick, although then it was known as Wick Farm.

By 1812, the estate of the Manor of Fingringhoe consisted of Fingringhoe Hall, Hall Farm, Hay Farm, Wick Farm and oyster beds and salt marshes: all told, a total of about 800 acres. The entire estate was sold in that year. Wick Farm – listed as Lot 4 – was described as 505 acres of rich arable and pasture, with a further 357 acres which included the Geydon (Geedon) saltings and also Rat Island, which is now a Trust reserve. Various parts of the farm were named Woodfield, Poundfield, Pittfield, Beaconfield, Great (and Little) Stonefield, The Meadow, and Great (and Little) Marsh. *Beaconfield* is particularly interesting. It has echoes of a local legend that the Romans had a signal station there, and centuries later local people were still calling the area Beacon Town.

Above: The Wick Farm stockyard is now the Centre carpark.
Below: Wick Farm cart tracks still survive because the gravel operators used them as roads.

Above: Sediment-settling ponds were important in the daily operation of the pit. Today, the Bunkhouse pond and others are superb wildlife features.

Below: Rusting sluices are a reminder of decades of turmoil that saw Wick Farm transformed into a barren moonscape.

In May 1904 the manor estate was sold once more. Wick Farm this time was Lot 2, and was described as a house, barn, cart stable for four horses, chaff house, loose box, two cattle yards and sheds, sheep yards and sheds, a fowl house and 515 acres of fertile arable, grassland and saltings. Seeing the isolation of the farm not as a liability but as a sales opportunity, the vendor thought *'part could be advantageously utilised for an explosive or chemical factory'*. The farm was sold again in 1921 to an unknown gravel extraction firm. By then, it had declined to about 100 acres, with the Geedon marsh having already been sold to the War Department, and three fields to a local farmer. The reference to the barn fits nicely with this narrative. It once stood on the site of the present Wildlife Garden, just outside the Visitor Centre. It was demolished by the Trust soon after The Wick became a nature reserve. The timber was reused to build the first of several Geedon hides. The total cost of the hide was six shillings – the price of a box of nails.

Freshwater Pit: Forty years of turmoil

After several tranquil centuries Wick Farm vanished into the mists of history, and was replaced by a lunar landscape of gravel workings. Large-scale extraction of the ice age gravel deposits began in 1928. Unlike today, when extraction moves efficiently along the line of a retreating cliff, the technology of the times saw piecemeal quarrying here, there, and in several other places – sometimes simultaneously. Spoil was heaped wherever it was convenient, and deposits of gravel were pursued wherever they lay. The result was a corrugated landscape of humps, bumps, trenches, gullies and holes. Everything that came out of the ground was washed before leaving the pit. Concrete and cement made from sand and ballast washed in sea water is inferior to the material that has been washed in fresh water. The Freshwater Sand and Ballast Co. named its new pit for that reason: it had access to lots of fresh water, and marketed its products accordingly. The central excavation in the pit – today's lake – was a reservoir essential to the whole operation. From there, water was supplied to wherever it was needed in the pit to wash soil from the sand and ballast.

The vital fresh water came from the sky, but more reliable sources were also used. On the northern, unexcavated boundary of the pit was a spring-fed pond, which survives to this day. Water was pumped from the pond to the reservoir to maintain the water level. The third source of fresh water came from deep underground. A well was dug close to the jetty. It pierced the sand and gravel, and then the London Clay beneath the estuary bed, and entered the chalk at a depth reputed to be about 60 ft. Water was pumped from the chalk uphill to the road level, from where it fell by gravity into the reservoir. The heavy pump stood on a massive concrete

Freshwater Pit 1961. The remains of a conveyor belt can be seen in the foreground leading into the large gravel screening building from where the photograph was taken. Today this is the picnic area. *Trust Archives.*

base, in a timber shed next to the well. We call it the Boathouse, but actually it is a pump house. To avoid wasting the water after the washing process had been carried out in different areas of the pit, special ponds were constructed where sediment was allowed to settle to the bottom. The cleaner water was then reused. Kit's pond, the Bunkhouse pond and several others that are now dry are all examples of old settling ponds.

Between 1940 and the end of the Second World War the pit was occasionally used for training by the army. There are accounts of a guard post at the end of the jetty, and the remains of a circular gun emplacement still lie in the nearby gorse. Local Territorials also used the

pit, and in two thickets you can still see their shallow, rectangular rifle pits. Tragically, some young soldiers drowned in the lake during a rubber boat exercise.

The concrete bunkers were the nucleus of the Freshwater Pit. Perched on top of them was a very large building containing gravel screening machinery. Travelling on conveyor belts from different areas of the pit, washed sand and ballast entered the building and was sorted into various products, which fell into the waiting bunkers below. Chutes delivered everything into trucks on a small railway which led to the end of the jetty where barges waited for their cargo. The jetty also had a travelling crane, and a conveyor belt. Between

1951 and 1959 when the pit closed, 250,000 cubic yards of gravel were shipped by barge from the Freshwater Pit to construct the oil refinery on the Isle of Grain in the Thames estuary.

The Picnic Area is a large flat area that was not excavated, and is at the same ground level as the old Wick Farm. The small blockhouse building nearby was the office of the gravel pit manager. Because so many Trust members asked to listen to nightingales late at night, the building was fitted with beds and renamed The Bunkhouse. Many people have fond memories of wandering the reserve in the small hours listening to the nightingales, and then retiring to The Bunkhouse to discover even more wildlife inside. The Bunkhouse was removed in 2003, but memories linger on of the giant spiders, the Elsan chemical loo, and the money-grabbing electricity meter.

The last conveyor belt clanked to a halt in 1959, and the Freshwater Pit also passed into history. There is a suggestion that at that time the Ministry of Defence wished to expand the Fingringhoe Training Ranges, and would have eagerly done so by buying the old pit in its completely unrestored state. The story goes that local people did not wish it to happen, and when the young Essex Naturalists' Trust threw its hat into the ring as a potential buyer, it received great local support which extended to guaranteeing the bank loan that the Trust needed to make the purchase. It may be true. Looking at the silent, torn landscape, the Trust knew it must buy. The old gravel workings were big, contained lots of water, and were located beside a major estuary. With its moon-like terrain, it was a blueprint for the nature reserve the Trust needed to really put itself on the map. And nature was waiting in the wings, ready to walk on-stage.

The barge *Centaur* is loaded with sand or ballast via the overhead conveyor. *Photograph: N. Hardinge.*

Chapter 3

The creation of a nature reserve: 1961–1964

In 2005 we are accustomed to the ongoing programme of reserve purchases and new visitor centres that has been both the mark of the Trust's success and an indicator of sources of funds that simply were not available in 1961. The purchase of the old gravel workings from Brightlingsea Aggregates that secured them as a Trust nature reserve must have been a moment of pure joy. What had we got for our money? There were various farm outbuildings that the Trust converted into an office and a workshop, and the house in which successive reserve wardens have lived. Originally a one-up, one-down

farm worker's cottage, it was later doubled in size. When Wick Farm became a gravel pit, a much larger house was added to the rear, making a single large structure for the use of the pit manager. There were also 125 acres of land. The Trust was soon hard at work planning just how we would make the chaotic wasteland a safe and attractive place for people to enjoy the wildlife that was likely to flood into the new nature reserve.

The original landscape was one of gently sloping farmland bordering the Colne, with a minor stream valley on its northern boundary. It was a farm typical of the 19th century, with

Wick Farm, 1961. The farm outbuildings were later incorporated into the Fingringhoe Wick Visitor Centre. *Trust Archives.*

The old sand martin cliff. One of the people in the picture is Ken Crawshaw, who organised the annual refacing of the cliff. *Trust Archives.*

arable fields and pastures divided by hedgerows. Several cart tracks wandered across the farm, and the gravel pit operators used sections of these as roads for moving ballast, plant and vehicles about the pit. The tracks now form sections of our nature trails. The Soil Survey studied the site in 1966. In their report, they observed that the excavated areas of the reserve are of exposed gravelly or clayey material in hundreds of heaps. In contrast, the undisturbed farmland soils on the north boundary are well-drained brown earth and gley soils influenced by water-logging in winter. Loess is at the surface in several areas. Almost the entire site is underlain by sand and gravel.

North-east Essex has a climate that has continental influences. It is warmer in summer and colder in winter than adjacent regions. The coastal position of The Wick however results in a lessening of temperature peaks and troughs. Prevailing winds are from the south-west, although cold and dry easterly or north-easterly winds can occur in spring. Essex is one of the driest counties: up to 1990, on average, The Wick received about 547 mm of rain annually, but since then rainfall – especially in winter – has become very erratic. The county has a particularly low humidity count, but the densely vegetated and sheltered excavations at The Wick produce a localised humidity that particularly benefits ferns, mosses and teeming invertebrates.

The work begins
The late Geoff Pyman and the late Stanley Jermyn were key people in those vital early years. With others,

they planned the nature reserve that later evolved from the wasteland, and shaped the all-important first management plan.

Geoff was then the Trust's Founder-Chairman. Stan Jermyn was elected to the Trust Council in 1960; later becoming General Secretary and Treasurer, he carried out the first survey of the wild plants growing at The Wick. Both of these committed and able men were in at the start. The first management plan for Fingringhoe Wick was a mixture of essential needs, possibilities and suggestions, but it nevertheless spelled out the exact same message of more complex plans 40 years later: *maintain the diversity*. Unlike the comparatively uniform ancient woodlands, flower-rich meadows and coastal marshland

reserves that are now the jewels in the Trust's crown, Fingringhoe Wick possessed a dozen major potential wildlife habitats, and scores of micro-habitats. Decades of man-made disturbance had produced features which later would attract a host of invertebrates and wild flowers, and numerous birds and mammals. With time of no account, spreads of sand became gorse heathland, dry gravel became grassland, wet bits turned into sallow thickets, and ponds filled with watery plants and insects. The late Clifford Owen was involved in the early planning, and was the first person to fill the warden's role and organise the first working parties of volunteers. With ferrets living with him in the house, he was truly in touch with nature.

An industrial wasteland. Somehow, volunteers and contractors cleared the new nature reserve of rusting and dangerous rubbish. *Trust Archives.*

Damaged by a ship, the end of the jetty is demolished by a team from HMS *Ganges*. *Trust Archives.*

There was a great deal of dangerous and unsightly scrap metal and rubbish to be removed: physical hazards had to be made safe, and there was endless work in creating facilities for the increasing number of visiting Trust members. Master-minded by the late Ken Crawshaw, the official Director of Works in the early 1960s, the work rolled on.

Improving the sandy beach for wildlife and converting the derelict and decaying ballast jetty into a walkway leading to our first jetty bird hide was an enormous task. Today, Crawshaw's Foreshore and a commemorative hide overlooking the salt marshes are a reminder of Ken and those pioneer working parties. The jetty was – and is – a hazard to shipping. In those days a hurricane lamp hanging on the end was maintained by the warden, although that didn't prevent a ship from colliding with the jetty one foggy night. A demolition exercise by a naval team from HMS *Ganges* blew the damaged section of the jetty to smithereens, terrifying birds and birdwatchers alike. Now, the red light on the jetty is powered by a solar panel. Because the jetty has become unsafe, the hide has been removed. Looking upriver from the jetty, the view is enhanced by the wreck of *Fly*, a ballast barge built in Appledore in Devon in 1899 for the purpose of working on the Colne. On their maiden voyage, sister barges *Bee* and *Ant* were lost off Dover in a storm which struck the trio on their way to Essex.

One of our Trust archive photographs shows a typically ambitious 1963 working party. In it, four people are working on the island in the lake, which originally had a humped, whaleback profile. The four volunteers are blithely making the island flat (for nesting duck) by removing four feet of soil along its entire length. In its fervour to remove as much evidence of the reserve's industrial origin as possible, the Trust called in the demolition squad once more. This time, the squad were army sappers, and the target was the concrete bunkers. Happily, the fourteen- inch reinforced concrete was more than a match for the explosives, and we still have the massive walls today to remind us of how it all began.

The blueprint becomes a reality

Recognising that members visiting their new nature reserve would like to see evidence of management to benefit wildlife as well as people, the Trust embarked on a programme of tree planting in the mid-1960s. A wide range of native species was planted in clumps, and to this day the survivors are recognised by the remains of ancient rabbit guards and rotted stakes. It is usual to find a planted oak or a birch with a six-inch diameter trunk growing next to a self-set tree twice as thick. The planting was really for effect – there was no conservation need to plant anything at all. In 2004 we are now witness to what natural succession can achieve in 40 years from a standing start, and the writing is on the wall: without systematic control of the oak, the nature reserve will eventually lose much of its diversity and wildlife and become fairly uniform woodland.

1974: Gwen Foott, Stewart Linsell and Fred Boot plan a nature trail feature. *Photograph: Roy Masefield.*

The Trust and the Forestry Commission jointly created a mixed woodland plantation of Scots pine, larch, holm oak and beech that one day, when the pines were mature, would be a useful cash crop. Years later it was decided instead to manage the plantation as a habitat for wildlife, and as a visual amenity for visitors. The trees had been planted in regulation density and in rows, so they had to be thinned. For very many years the vital work of turning the plantation into woodland to benefit wildlife and enhance the nature reserve was carried out by Tony Marshall. Working on his own in the trees on winter afternoons, Tony single-handedly shaped the Marshall's Plantation we know today. Armed with a bow saw and a rickety ladder, he removed countless trees to give the others room to grow. He is one of the legendary figures at The Wick.

Private: Members only

Long ago, Fingringhoe Wick was private property, visited only by members of Essex Naturalists' Trust. Later, after a lot of debate, the public was also allowed in – but only as far as the lake, where they were stopped by the famous Members' Gate. European Conservation Year in 1970 helped recruitment of Trust members – for an annual subscription of £1 – but they were outnumbered three to one by the public, who paid three shillings to get in. It was decided that Sunday must be *Members Only*. Stewart Linsell, who was the fourth warden, asked members to place their membership car stickers in the rear window and to park facing the river so that on his day off he could use his binoculars to see if any non-members had gate-crashed. Visitors entering the reserve by road passed both the warden's house and his office, so almost certainly he would see them. Invaders from the estuary however were a more difficult problem, because they were invisible to the warden. A huge sign was erected on the beach telling passing yachtsmen that Essex Naturalists' Trust did not want people to land. Naturism was new and exciting then, and the sign acted like a magnet until the truth sank in.

A grisly episode occurred when it was decided to bury Epping Forest deer road-kill carcases in the soil, to enable decomposition to remove all the flesh so that the clean skeletons could be used for study purposes. It all went wrong when foxes dug up the deer and dismembered them. For weeks, horrified visitors were tripping over bloody heads and ripped-off legs.

A growing Trust: 1965–1975

The Trust used the surviving old farm outbuildings to good effect. Visitors entered the warden's office to check in and chat. Like every warden's office it was full of skulls, fossils, owl pellets, muddy boots and battered old Barbour jackets. After finding out what birds had been seen, visitors struck out into the reserve. The Green Trail was the first nature trail to be laid out: the Blue Trail followed later when non-members of the Trust were admitted.

Despite the tree planting aberration, the influential Trust officers who made the decisions at The Wick were determined that the new reserve would be managed as scientifically as possible, and that it would be a showcase example of a Trust nature reserve, for wildlife and for people. The late Vivian Robson became Trust Chairman in 1967, and held office until 1987. Headmaster of Honywood School, 'Robbie' was also a dedicated naturalist. He saw the possibility of The Wick as a valuable education tool for visiting schools. From the outset, it had also been seen as a study area, where the initially slow but then rapid colonisation of the old gravel workings by the first plants, insects and animals would be recorded. This strong emphasis on education has continued to the present day, and we now have a staff Education Officer and welcome dozens of school groups

every year. A great deal of wildlife recording was done in those early years, and it has continued, although in a less concentrated form.

The outbuildings at The Wick were barely large enough for the warden's needs. As the Trust expanded and became ever more immersed in its work, elected officers had to keep all their paperwork at home. At the beginning of what has since turned out to be a ceaseless conveyor-belt of escalating environmental threats, there was also a growing need to spread the conservation message and to involve the public. The pressures resulted in the Trust mounting a successful appeal for funds to build a Visitor Centre at Fingringhoe Wick. This was to be our first Centre, and it was going to be built in our first nature reserve. The decision reflects the Trust's belief in itself; however, if it was not actually a step in the dark, it was certainly an act of faith.

Fingringhoe Wick Visitor Centre has helped raise public awareness of escalating threats to wildlife.

Chapter 4

Natural succession: The big greening

In photographs taken in the mid-1960s you can see that much of the once-bare ground supports willowherbs, field poppy, marsh thistle, ragwort, bristly ox-tongue and a host of other agricultural 'weeds' from the surrounding countryside. Wet sand and clay at the edge of the lake is home to colt's-foot, marsh horsetail and rushes. There is also the first evidence of woodland at The Wick. Young thickets of sallow and crack willow are visible in wet hollows among the old excavations, and at the edges of the settling ponds. Birch is widely scattered on the drier slopes. To the eye of the visitor at the time it was more attractive than the raw and barren pit. Purists might argue that leaving the colonisation of the bare ground entirely to nature was the best course to take: without doubt however the arrival of trees – planted or naturally seeded – was welcomed by most people.

The highlight of the nature reserve in the early years was our renowned sand martin cliff. Over 300 pairs of martins nested for years in a long cliff at the rear of the main Heath. These industrious little birds are perhaps the epitome of gravel pit wildlife. They need vertical cliffs for nesting,

The lake in the 1960s. The two pointed conifers are growing in the garden of the warden's house. *Trust Archives.*

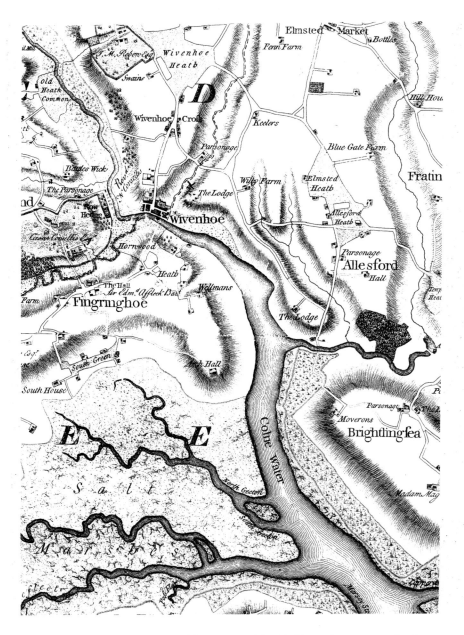

From the 1777 map of Essex by Chapman and André. The nature reserve lies to the left of the river, roughly at the tip of the peninsular in the centre of the map. Arch Hall no longer exists. *Courtesy Essex Record Office.*

and colonies return from Africa early in the spring to nest in the same cliff they have used for many years. Sand martins like an open, treeless site where they can hawk for insects and have an unimpeded flight path onto the face of the cliff where they make their nest burrows. When the gravel operators ceased cutting into the cliff face, it quickly deteriorated: wind, rain and frost caused it to collapse along its length, and the nest burrows became vulnerable to stoats and weasels. There is an archive photograph showing Geoff Pyman supervising a group of teenagers trying to remove tons of fallen sand and gravel to restore the vertical cliff face before the martins arrived. Each year the problem was worse, and eventually the martins abandoned our cliff and colonised the very long cliff face being actively worked by Thames and Colne Aggregates just a few hundred yards away. By 2005, our old cliff was just another gentle, scrub-covered slope.

The woodland arrives

Within a few years the thickets merged, and belts of secondary woodland dominated The Wick. When the pit was working, water for washing the sand and gravel was pumped or channelled into ponds, trenches, culverts and the main lake. The excavations are lower than ground level, and rain and ground water accumulated in wet winters so that the gravel workings had a high water table. Pumping ceased when the pit closed in 1959. With the invasion of large numbers of water-sucking trees – sallows, willows and, later, alder – the reserve began to dry out. Birch spread widely as a result, and the first oaks appeared. The drying out of the reserve has continued to this day. It is interesting to see the different types of woodland that have formed, each a direct result of the conditions that existed when the pit closed down.

Spreads of dry gravel now support dense hawthorn thickets. Well-drained, sunny spoil heaps have stands of birch on their slopes. Winter-wet soils at the foot of the heaps are home to thickets of sallow, whilst oaks are perched on the dry summits in pole position to eventually dominate everything beneath them. This natural selection of growth sites by various species is typical, and predictable. Groves of aspen flourish in two areas where they are spreading via suckers: a group of planted hybrid grey willows however is slowly dying out. The Trust planted alders next to the stream in the old grazing meadow, and beside the lake – a decision that is causing increasing problems for both sites as the years pass. Sweet chestnut trees were planted close to the lake bird hides in a sensible plan to make the reserve self-sufficient in fence posts, stakes, rails and other costly items. Grey squirrels love the nuts. They forget where they bury them, and young chestnuts regularly pop up a long way from the parent trees. Inexplicably, Lombardy poplars were planted in two sites, and beech was planted in the heavy clay soil of the old grazing meadow and along the path to Kit's pond. Fragments of Wick Farm hedgerows still survive. Elm and field maple are both sure indicators that a thicket is actually a piece of a long-vanished farm hedge. There is even a single, lonely spindle – a shrub usually found in old woodland edges and old hedgerows.

Ancient traces

Since Neolithic farmers cleared the original primeval wildwood, woodland has probably waxed and waned at The Wick more times than we realise. The last period of extensive tree cover may have followed the Black Death, when much of the countryside was depopulated. There is some evidence of historic woodland at The Wick. Dog's mercury is a traditional indicator of ancient woodland, and a colony exists in the hedgerow on the north

boundary that was never excavated. It conjures up a vision of woodland that may have once extended north up the Colne, across land that is now arable farm fields. 'Ghost' woodlands and hedgerows that leave their enigmatic traces for people to attempt to decipher centuries later are common in our ravaged countryside today. A more tangible feature exists in the form of the giant pollarded oak that grows next to the Scrape. It is far and away the oldest tree at The Wick. The famous map of Essex produced by Chapman and André in 1777 (see p. 26) shows the site of the present day nature reserve ending as a steep bluff above the Colne. The bluff was probably wooded and unlikely to have been farmed. Possibly this small wood was a surviving piece of the woodland which may have covered the whole area before it

1972. Gorse and scrub burn near Kit's pond after being ignited by stubble-burning in an adjacent field. *Trust Archives.*

became a farm. It's only a theory, but it seems possible, and it is reinforced by the presence of a very large hazel – another indicator of old woodland. Today, the steep slope and these two ancient trees above the Scrape are all that remains of the 18th-century bluff.

When woodland claimed the once-bare gravel workings, woodland wildlife responded. In succession, tawny owl, all three woodpeckers, grey squirrel, sparrowhawk, speckled wood butterfly, badger, little owl and numerous woodland invertebrates and fungi moved in. All – except for the lesser spotted woodpecker – are now established, and they have been joined by many others. Woodland encroaching on the gorse-dominated Kit's pond area was stopped in its tracks in the summer of 1972 by a runaway stubble fire. About fifteen acres were turned to charcoal. Seven fire engines took thousands of gallons of water from the lake to kill the fire.

The inferno was not a complete disaster: the gorse regenerated vigorously in 1973, and best of all, the NFU was forced to establish the first code of practice governing how farmers should safely burn stubble in the future. In his daily log, Stewart Linsell's report for the day of the fire – 1 September 1972, or Black Friday – makes doleful reading. A subsequent sombre entry records the death of Stanley Jermyn in 1973. He was a vital force that helped shape the Trust, and his energy and expertise was going to be missed. As Vivian Robson said;

'Stan Jermyn was the Essex Naturalists' Trust'.

Man in the hot seat: The warden

Stewart Linsell was one of six wardens who have managed The Wick, and whose combined efforts have produced the nature reserve we know today. Clifford Owen was the first. A gamekeeper who liked living and working with ferrets and polecats, he was also the curator of Colchester Natural History Museum. The late Major Paddy Lunt became our second warden in 1965. Paddy was the man who laid out the paths that wander across the nature reserve. There are old archive photographs showing him sitting proudly beside the Roman flagon he unearthed in the garden; of him using a tractor to lower the Telegraph Bridge into place; of him standing with his wife Patricia beside the nest of a mute swan in the reedy Boathouse pond. Paddy retired in 1967 and was replaced by Harry Sutton. I am sad that I have learned nothing of Harry or his exploits.

Stewart Linsell was the next warden into the hot seat, and the first to be paid. He and his wife Kay moved into the house in 1969, and Stewart quickly made his mark both as a naturalist, and as a man of action. He saw an opportunity to create a new feature at The Wick which would benefit wildlife, and which would also be an attraction to visitors. The new habitat – a shallow, brackish lagoon with nesting islands – was named the Scrape, after its famous large cousin at Minsmere. Work began in 1972. The nature of the work and the scale of operation called for lots of willing hands. Volunteers were needed in quantity, and Stewart possessed the charm to attract them and to keep them coming. Excavating a two-acre wader pool in a salt marsh is cold, muddy, heavy and exhausting work. I know – I was one of Stewart's volunteers. I recall looking at him and thinking *'he is getting paid to live in this nature reserve and to look after wildlife'*. As a jaded London commuter at the time I never knew that such a great job could exist. Stewart and Kay moved to Hickling Broad in 1975.

They were replaced by Malcolm Wright and his wife Rosemary. Malcolm was a keen ornithologist with previous experience at the key bird reserves at the Calf of Man, and Bardsey Island. In his eyes, the reserve lacked areas of scrub and woodland which would attract a wider variety of birds to The Wick. Scrub was good and should be encouraged – and at that period in the history of the reserve there was no reason to think otherwise. He took a keen interest in recording the birds at The Wick, and assisted Administrative Officer Phil Murton in ringing many birds over the years using mist nets. Phil was a qualified ringer and he caught the legendary 'Flagpole Freddie' – a male nightingale trapped each May for five successive years in the same thicket. In 1979 Malcolm departed for the National Nature Reserve at Caerlaverock in Dumfries, and I was appointed warden of Fingringhoe Wick.

Hawthorn *(left)* and bramble *(right)* are important to wildlife in spring, summer and autumn. They are key species in the scrub habitat at The Wick.

Chapter 5
Living at The Wick

Wick Farm is a happy house. I do not know why, it just is. We felt it when we moved in, and the happiness is still there. I have spoken to several people who have lived in the house; farm workers, gravel pit people and several previous Trust wardens all sensed the same. Now that we are leaving, a lot of memories come flooding back.

Nature reserve wardens make bad gardeners, because we are too interested in the weeds in the flowerbed, in nibbling insects and in the mosses in the lawn. To make things worse, our garden at The Wick is doubly horticulturally-challenged because it is so much a part of the reserve, without fencing. We like the way the garden flows out into the nature reserve, and the way the marsh landscape flows in. The down side however is that it is wide open to every rabbit, badger, fox, muntjac, pheasant, moorhen and mallard that all use the garden as though it were theirs, which of course it is.

The winter of 1982 was long and icy. Driving daughter Donna to catch the bus in the village one morning, I slid into an Eastern National bus and wrote off our car. Every dark, freezing morning for a week after that, Gina and the children piled into the trailer and I drove the tractor to the village

Swamp stonecrop is an invasive alien plant, and will survive efforts like this to remove it. Chemical control is too damaging. *Trust Archives.*

so they could catch the bus. With mud and slush spraying all over them, my nearest and dearest began their day dressed from head to toe in bin liners.

Gina is great at DIY, which is lucky, because I am fairly useless. She once spent a whole week putting up new wallpaper in our bedroom. A couple of days later a starling came down the chimney. Trying to fly to freedom, it made a circuit of the room, and 'splashed' all four walls. It was September, and he had been gorging on blackberries for a week.

For fifteen years our family lived with a beautiful short-haired pointer called Stonyways Fortune Cookie. She didn't have a great IQ, but she had great charm and a world-beating nose that could scent a pheasant – or a Mars bar – at 50 paces. One day we found her 'pointing' in the bathroom, at a large rat beneath the bath. A few months later that same bath was home to ten orphan shelducklings. Cookie was also a keen angler and liked nothing better than to sit next to our son Jonathan on the bank of the lake, intently watching the bobbing float. She was bitten by an adder, and survived. We were once given a pet jackdaw, and until we were forced reluctantly to pass him on to another unsuspecting household, 'Jack' ruled the roost. The average jackdaw is smarter than the average pointer, and Cookie became his dive-bombing target from the first day. Jonathan once found himself being followed by a brood of very young mallard

ducklings who thought he was mum. It was only resolved by him rowing them around the lake in the boat to show them what mum really looked like, and dropping them over the side.

One spring, all four chimneys were invaded by colonies of honeybees. Mistakenly, we tried to smoke them out of one chimney: result, one sooty, smoky bedroom full of very angry bees. There was a memorable visit I made to the vet with a convalescent heron inside a huge box. As I sat in the waiting room surrounded by people with small boxes and cages containing ailing budgies and tortoises, my box was the centre of attention, although nobody actually asked what was inside. When my turn came I stood up; the bottom of the box promptly collapsed and a pair of great scaly legs shot out. And then there was that time I mislaid a grass snake in the house, and Gina got a steely glint in her eye ...

'How lovely to live in a nature reserve'

Not everyone feels comfortable with the isolation and the wild landscape around the house. It is intimidating to some, and makes others feel insecure. Most people however eye the house and its surroundings and claim they would love to live there. It has been perfect for us. Through the seasons and the years we have seen the daily, run-of-the-mill masterpieces that nature produces so effortlessly: cloud shapes, light effects, sunsets and storms. Gentle, golden sunlight that turned the estuary and salt

The Geedon salt marsh is a salty garden of great beauty in a vast landscape.

marshes to something like Eden; ice floes in the Colne; brutal, freezing days when a glaze of ice formed on the exposed mudflats and wading birds died; days when gales made the overhead electricity cables howl from dawn to dusk; winter nights when Orion hung overhead and the estuary glittered in silvery moonlight.

Night time at The Wick is full of sounds. Curlew, grey plover and redshank can clearly be heard from the house windows. When the falling tide exposes the mud, they must feed, even if a blizzard is blowing and it is 1.00 am. Brent geese can be heard muttering and nattering out on the Geedon marsh. Barking foxes, yelping little owls and hooting tawnies make up a typical night. From February onwards, the black-headed gulls return to their breeding site on Rat Island and begin a raucous night and day chorus that does not stop until they disperse in late summer. Sometimes, the nocturnal Wick is absolutely silent, like a giant animal holding its breath. Sometimes, I hear sounds that are so strange and unknown they might have come from Mars. From the lake comes the splash of jumping fish in the summer: in winter the sound of whistling wigeon. The rushing night wind in the dark springtime thickets cannot drown the sound of the famous Wick nightingales.

It is not as dark as I would like. Light pollution is already a global problem, and in Essex we have our share. North, there is a glow above Colchester: south, there is a lesser glow from Brightlingsea. Flashing lights in mid-river are from buoys marking the deep water channel for shipping. In the 1980s and 1990s we would be woken in the early hours by the deep thudding of diesel engines as ships came and went on the Colne at high tide. The loss-making Hythe harbour closed years ago, and now the only working vessels on the Colne are the Thames and Colne Aggregates ballast ships, fishing boats from Wivenhoe and the occasional charter barge on a bird-watching trip.

The neighbours

We – and the Trust – have been lucky with the neighbours. Chris Rowe owns the fields south of the reserve, and he and the entire Cock family, who farm the land have always been helpful, especially when we badly needed overspill car parking space for Open Days and other fund-raising events. Chris Rowe, the father of Chris junior, drew up the plans that were needed when the gravel operators added the large house at the rear of Wick Farm in 1932. Chris Rowe senior was anything but an intensive farmer, and would ask me to find and mark the nests of peewits and oystercatchers in his crops before tractor work was done. The late Mrs Wynne-Eaton lived in nearby Marsh Cottage, and made herself responsible for the regular clearance of tide-borne rubbish from the beach.

Jacqueline Wolfers lives at Jaggers Farm, and is our nearest neighbour. A friend for many years, she is lucky enough to have an old farm pond surrounded by willows, and in 2003 undertook management work that will ensure the future of this historic Fingringhoe village feature. Jacqueline and her son are a part of Trust history: in 1973 she received an award as our 5000th member. Zélie Joplin and Peter and Dulcie Hewitt live in South Green Road, and have been our friends and supporters of The Wick for a long time. Norman and Caroline Priestley also live in South Green Road. They lent us their sheep to improve the management of our grassland, and Norman – the Trust warden of neighbouring Rat Island – took me on a memorable boat trip to this most isolated and inaccessible of our reserves.

Ministry of Defence land stretches away south, towards Mersea Island. I cannot exaggerate its importance to wildlife, to our nature reserve on its doorstep, and to the human eye in terms of landscape. Under enlightened MoD management for many years, the Geedon and Fingringhoe salt marshes and the Langenhoe Marsh are all part of the Colne Estuary Site of Special Scientific Interest. Successive Head Range Wardens were Vic Cawley and Ray Giles. More recently, this key post has been held by the industrious Chico Duncan. A man of great energy, Chico has done great work on the Langenhoe Marsh to clear invading scrub, raise water levels and bring back extensive reedbeds that once flourished on the marsh. Due to his efforts, the marsh harrier and bearded tit are now regular breeders on the marsh, and hopes are high that the bittern may over-winter, and then breed there.

We are just as lucky with our neighbours to the north. Thames and Colne Aggregates has an award-winning reputation in the quarrying industry for health and safety, and for environmental awareness. The company has a proven commitment to the local environment, and ensures that its day-to-day extraction operation has virtually no impact on Fingringhoe parish. Active quarrying has resulted in a long, high cliff where several hundred pairs of sand

martins have nested for decades. The company has also planted new woodland and created new lakes as an amenity for local people, and to boost wildlife. Large areas of flower-rich new grassland have been sown. Justifiably, Thames and Colne Aggregates are pleased that marsh harriers breed on their land, and keep a watchful eye on the nest site.

Wardens of the nature reserve have always been reminded by villagers that in the past, as children, they used to love swimming from the beach close to the jetty. In the friendliest way, older people from the village often remind us that our beach was once their beach.

The wreck of the *Fly* on the beach near Robbie's Hide.

Chapter 6

Walking with nightingales

It is 2.00 am and The Wick is very, very dark. The thickets are silent, and the air is full of the heavy scent of hawthorn blossom. Curlew call from the Colne mudflats. It is so quiet you might think there is not a nightingale for 100 miles. The sudden burst of song – loud, aggressive and very close – is answered immediately from the other side of the path. For nightingale *aficionados,* this is the perfect setting: two males in adjacent territories, with females to impress and with attitude. The duet sets off all the neighbours, and within minutes I count eight males filling the night air with song. From past experience, I know that a ripple of song will have passed from thicket to thicket, and although I cannot hear them, many other nightingales are also singing in distant territories. Suddenly, silence falls. These pauses are part of the performance for the listener, and add dramatic contrast to the concert.

Gina and I have lived with the nightingales at The Wick for 26 years. In that time, hundreds of nightingales have fledged and migrated to West Africa each autumn. There, our nocturnal songster is just another small, brown bird trying not to draw attention to itself as it flits through the humid thickets that flank those muddy African rivers. At winter's end, and prompted by their biological clock, the males make a long journey to Europe to breed. The females follow later, and from 1 April expectations and questions from visitors mount daily: *'Have they arrived yet?'* Daily I visit the thickets where year after year the first males have sung. Daily I am more convinced that disaster has struck: our nightingales have been trapped and pickled in Malta, or shot in Spain. The sad thing is, some have. And then – what relief – *'They're back!'*

That small, brown bird is now driven by his urge to breed. First, he must claim a territory and hold it secure against other males: if he fails, he may also fail to attract a female, and the whole wonderful feat of migration will have been wasted. The thicket throbs with song. Liquid, deep and loud, the male nightingale fires machine gun-like bursts of superb song at his rivals in the surrounding bushes. He is invisible, and when they respond to his challenge, so are they. Singing nightingales are immobile, and I have lost count of the number of visitors who, awed by the power of the song pouring from the thickets, turn to me in despair and say *'will we ever see one?'* The male sings, with breaks for feeding, on and off around the clock. He uses his voice both as a seductive lure to females, and as an effective weapon to deter rivals.

Luckily, it is music to our ears.

In 2004 over 30 males were counted at The Wick. The people on the tours that I lead in the first two weeks of May – Nightingale Fortnight – are thrilled by what they hear. I don't think they believe me when I tell them that the birds they are listening to at dusk will be singing hard at midnight; at 2.00 am; in the dawn chorus and on and off every day for weeks to come. At times I find it hard to believe myself. Every tour starts at 7.30 pm. With about 180 previous tours under my belt, I have learned the hard way that nothing nightingales do can be guaranteed; there are too many variables in play. Gathered outside the Centre and with the rudd rising in the lake behind me, I introduce myself; then the Trust, The Wick – and the nightingale. Some of the people around me have heard all this several times on tours in other years, but to their credit they still laugh at the right moments. I promise – *I guarantee* – everybody that tonight they will hear nightingales, and that by dusk they will have shared an experience they will tell their friends about.

These people are looking forward to something special: they have paid to join the tour and some have come from far corners of Essex, and beyond. They are happy and relaxed. I can feel the usual knot of anxiety beginning to

Nightingale at the nest. *Photograph: David and Eric Hosking.*

form. Wildlife rambles of the *'let's see what's about'* variety that I sometimes lead are easy compared to this, where the target is very specific. I tell them that today the first male nightingale might be heard almost immediately we leave the lake, but tomorrow it could be a long time before that magical moment happens. But happen it will: have faith in your leader.

Sure enough, tonight is one of those white-knuckle tours that justify my small knot of anxiety. We walk; we talk, we laugh and joke. We see a badger latrine, a colony of orchids, a barn owl, muntjac tracks – and we keep on walking and talking. Could this evening be my first-ever complete failure? Ahead, there is a thickety territory where just this morning a nightingale poured his song into the May sunshine. Silence – total silence. Can there be such a thing as a malevolent nightingale? We walk on, and are 40 yards away when suddenly he unleashes a string of rapid-fire notes that send us scurrying back for more. Within a minute, his neighbours respond to his outburst, and the thickets soon throb with deep and liquid song. The bird was just one of many we heard that night.

Why does the nightingale do it? What advantage is there in the male singing so loudly, so often and by the light of the moon as well as the sun? If dawn to dusk suits the singing blackbird, robin and song thrush, why should the nightingale be different? This is a bird that has inspired writers, poets and musicians. The ancient Greeks knew and loved the nightingale: their olive groves and gardens must have attracted them, and they still do today. The nightingale is a beautiful voice in the night, and it would be a shame if we could explain away its mystery with mundane ornithological facts. Come and hear them for yourself in April and May at Fingringhoe Wick. It's the place where nightingales sing.

Chapter 7

A maturing landscape: 1975–1979

The Fingringhoe Visitor Centre was officially opened in 1975 by the late Lord Greenwood of Rossendale, a former Cabinet Minister. As one of the first centres to be opened by a county wildlife trust it received a lot of enthusiastic support and media publicity. The new Centre was also the Trust headquarters: it housed the small core of professional staff responsible for the county-wide administration of the Trust and all its business. The late Squadron Leader Philip Murton had been appointed Administrative Officer in 1974. The late Bron Taylor, his secretary and part-time Field Officer Brian Watts were appointed in 1975. The nature reserve was managed by Malcolm Wright.

It was essential for the Trust to possess a Visitor Centre. The new building would bring in the public, and people would see at first-hand what we actually did and grasp why wildlife and the countryside were under threat. They would also understand our need for their support. The theme *'getting across the conservation message'* was important, as was *'catching them whilst they are young'* – the driving force behind our educational activity with schoolchildren, which, decades later, is going from strength to strength. A successful Centre would also clearly be a fine tool for recruiting new members and generating income.

The finished building was a focal point for a whole range of activities organised by the industrious and ambitious Colchester local Trust group. Annual Craft Fairs and Art Exhibitions attracted lots of people, funds and publicity for the Trust and its work.

Taking stock

When I took up my post in 1979 it took me a while to familiarise myself with the nature reserve, and to make an inventory of tools and equipment. Like a lot of people who are volunteers, during my days of action with Stewart Linsell's working party I knew only the places where we worked. Most of the reserve was unknown to me, and those early days of exploration were very exciting. Although the Trout Pool is a large and obvious feature today, it was the best part of a year before I found it, thanks to the young forest of tall willow and sallow that grew on every side.

There is an archive photograph showing Stewart driving a yellow machine looking a little like a golf buggy. The machine is the famous Brott – a ride-on grass cutter that he, and later Malcolm, both used to cut the grass tracks, and which could also pull a small load in a trailer. They loved it. I definitely did not, mainly because it could only cut grass on level surfaces, which, to be fair was what it was made for.

Within a month I asked the Trust for funds to buy the machine that I knew from my days with the National Trust was what The Wick needed in 1979. To its credit, the Trust gave its new warden the money. I bought the 10 hp Wolsey Clearway Hydrostatic rotary mower in 1979 for £1500 – a colossal expense for the Trust in those days. Always regarded as the prince of pedestrian mowers, it went out of production many years ago. My belief is that having created a perfect, powerful and robust mower that will demolish gorse and young trees with the same ease that it cuts your lawn, the company found itself with no new customers. Everybody who

needed a machine as good as theirs bought one – and still has it. Mine is still going strong after 26 years. In rapid succession a chainsaw, brush cutter and a venerable yellow Massey Ferguson three-cylinder diesel tractor and flail were added to the fighting strength. The 47 hp tractor is now 34 years old and still going well. All this equipment was necessary to counter rampant natural succession, which inevitably will result in uniform woodland if unchecked.

Understanding the landscape

The Wick nature reserve is just the latest of several uses to which the land has been put. Traces of earlier incarnations are numerous. Each previous existence has had some effect on the wildlife, and each has left physical evidence to remind us of the

1999, the north salt marsh.

past. It was important for me to grasp the full story, because future work to improve the reserve depended on a knowledge of the features that were really significant. Also, all wardens are expected to know absolutely everything, and it helps if you can answer at least 50% of the questions.

There was a lot to learn. Why is this pond square? Why is that a thicket of elm and not hawthorn like its neighbours? Why do the grass tracks on the north boundary have to be mown in the summer, but no others? What did this rusty old pipe once do? How did the concrete bunkers operate? It was, and is an endless quest. As soon as I think I have assembled most of the jigsaw, the arrival of an unexpected missing piece starts me off again. The year 2000 saw us clearing the high peninsular above the lake. The work involved an excavator removing a huge quantity of what I assumed was sandy gravel and spoil from the old pit. I was amazed to find that most of it was dumped topsoil. There was also clear evidence that somebody had used the area as an illegal landfill site 50 years ago. Roman rubbish is fine – but not tin cans and Marmite bottles.

In that first spring Gina and I heard the nightingales. They nested at The Wick even before it became a nature reserve. The female builds her nest less than three feet from the ground in dense cover, whilst the male needs scattered, bushy trees as his song posts. They often feed in adjacent areas which are relatively bare at ground level. To get thick, low vegetation you first need sunlight. This shopping list of the needs of the nightingale clearly suits a wide range of other wildlife as well, especially small mammals and invertebrates, and it was obvious that systematic coppicing of the deteriorating thickets was a top priority.

Backed by the ever-supportive Geoff Pyman, who was Chairman of the then Reserves Administration Committee, the principle tenet of the Management Plan, *maintain the diversity* was reborn. Like Stewart Linsell in his time, I needed a lot of willing hands to stop woodland encroaching on the ponds, grassland, heaths and reedbeds. There was also the need to restore all the fine views of the estuary, salt marshes and farmland that enhance visits to the reserve. Geoff gave me complete freedom of action to do what was required within the Management Plan – but I needed help.

Coffee, with cuts and grazes

It's Fingringhoe Wick, so this must be Sunday. Every Sunday morning, every autumn and winter, every year, the pattern repeats itself. I got into the Sunday-morning-at-The-Wick mind-set as a volunteer in 1972, and met others who had been doing it for years before I arrived. Driving home to Tiptree where we lived at the time, I would be muddy, tired and usually blood-stained. Working in the advertising agency in London the next day I found it hard to believe what I had been up to the previous day. They say that doing something that is totally different is therapeutic, and it certainly was for me. For years we had the benefit of a hard-working group of teenagers from Philip Morant school, led by teacher Ken Farquar. One icy day, as we stood on the frozen Trout Pool thawing out with hot coffee, I thought it would be nice to take a team photograph of the school group with the regular volunteers. There were about fifteen people in the viewfinder. Just as everything looked perfect, there was a loud crack. No, the ice didn't break, but they scattered in every direction, so I never got the photograph. I once suffered the humiliation of being dragged from the battlefield in my own trailer. Crouching low to light a fire on the east Heath, the cartilage in a knee locked. It was agony. After a while, the ambulance arrived but couldn't get nearer than the Picnic area. I was put in the trailer – what ignomy! The ambulance man driving the tractor said it was the best call-out he had had for years.

The volunteers who became my friends are fixed in the same Sunday-morning mind-set. Charities such as county wildlife trusts can only flourish if they are supported by volunteers, and individual nature reserves like The Wick are also heavily dependent on them. Between 1979 and 2005 I had the support of a team of people who helped make the reserve what it is today. Like their predecessors, the names of Arnold, Jim, David, Terry, John, Chris, Anne, Ray and Jo are written in The Wick's Hall of Glory.

Half past ten is coffee time. It's not much of break, but it splits the

Volunteers lay shingle on an island in the Scrape. *Photograph: David Baylis.*

The Freshwater Pit. The overhead conveyor delivered sand and ballast to barges at the end of the jetty. The roof of the Boathouse can be seen in front of the tree.

Photograph: N. Hardinge.

morning into two sessions, and everyone has a nice natter. We try to leave lots of logs and branches to rot down as deadwood habitats, but sometimes we just have to have a fire to create working space. I am pretty good at lighting fires, but I am more than pleased to delegate the whole job to another.

The members of the team share a love of wildlife and of the reserve, but we all have another thing in common: we are getting older by the day. Occasionally a youngster will join us from Writtle or Otley Agricultural Colleges as part of their training, but then they disappear. No matter how much they may like the work, who can blame them for preferring to seek younger people elsewhere? Put simply, the Trust cannot operate at its best without volunteers on our reserves, in our Centres and doing the 101 activities that not only save Trust resources, but free staff to do their jobs better.

Chapter 8

Winners and losers

The nature reserve is full of wildlife. Knowing what species are present, and where they are is vital. With that information we can confidently take steps to help many species by maintaining habitats that are deteriorating, and we can do our best to limit the spread of other species that are highly invasive or alien. There is not a lot that is 'natural' about a nature reserve, because the whole concept of selecting habitats and species to prosper at the expense of others is man-made. Nevertheless, the general condition of wildlife is so poor in the 21st century that nature reserves – or islands of wildlife – are the only hope for very many species. Taking regular inventories of all the species at The Wick is an impossible task, because the people qualified to survey say, the mosses, snails, hoverflies or midges are very few indeed, and they have a lot of ground to cover at other reserves and in the countryside.

The penultimate section of this book is a summary of much of The Wick's wildlife by a group of people who are expert in their various fields of interest. Inevitably, there are gaps in our knowledge: you can never find an expert on leeches when you need one. One of my first actions in 1979 was to examine the plant species list compiled by Stan Jermyn in 1962/ 1963. Two years later I made my own survey. I am a plant-hunter rather than a botanist like Stan Jermyn, but nevertheless I identified about 350 species of trees, shrubs, flowering plants, ferns and horsetails. The total tallied closely with Stan's – and yet there were large differences between the two lists. He surveyed a Wick of open, sunlit gravel workings, whilst 20 years later I surveyed a reserve full of shaded thickets and scrub. This example can be paralleled by a comparison of the insects and other invertebrates, and to a lesser degree by the birds, mammals, reptiles, amphibians and fungi.

The passage of time at The Wick has brought physical changes to many habitats, which are reflected by the wildlife. Changes in the habitats as a result of encroaching scrub and woodland over the past 40 years account for most of the winners and losers, but there are other forces at work.

Highs and lows: Wildlife and the weather

Short-term weather effects can prove the final straw for an insect or plant already on the verge of vanishing from the reserve. We have experienced four spells of Arctic weather when we have been snowed-in, and on two of those there were ice floes in the Colne. The great storm of 1987 blew down a few trees, but the

Badger numbers have increased at The Wick and they are doing well.

stress on many of the survivors was enough to weaken and eventually kill many more a long time after. The great drought year of 1976 killed the aquatic plants and animals in many ponds which dried up completely. More recently, winter rainfall was erratic and sparse between 1990 and 1995. Apart from its effect on the lake and ponds, the thickets of sallow and willow which were so dominant at one time began to disappear as these water-dependent species gave way to birch and oak. The hot and dry summer of 2003 shrivelled and withered the scrub by August, so that thickets usually heavily laden with seeds, berries and nuts were almost bare by autumn. That sort of summer may become common in the future.

Eventually, with the developing woodland continuing to suck the water from the soil, sallows and willows may be placed on the list of losers, with many others which we

lost years ago: grasshopper warbler, sedge warbler, sand martin, twite, redpoll, willow tit, wild angelica, blue fleabane, dingy skipper and grayling butterflies and, very recently, yellowhammer and reed bunting. Oak and birch are well placed on the winners list, with the rabbit, badger, grey squirrel, sparrowhawk, tawny owl, swamp stonecrop and speckled wood. Some species are in slow decline, whilst others seem to wax and wane cyclically. In short, the wildlife population is absolutely normal, and responding to changes and events that are bad for some, but good for others.

Wildlife casualties

Winners and losers can be entire species, and they can also be individuals. Within a month of moving in at The Wick I was brought

The reed bunting is in serious decline in Essex. One or two pairs still nest at The Wick. *Photograph: David Harrison.*

Avocets now breed in Essex and are seen daily on the mudflats. Once they were rare spring and autumn visitors to the Colne. *Photograph: David Harrison.*

an injured feral pigeon. I kept it for a while until it was fit, and then it was released. The following day I was given an emaciated fieldfare with a broken wing, which I could only put down. They were just the forerunners of over 100 bird casualties that came to me in five years. Amazingly, they represented 42 species. The winners/losers pattern had already been set by the first two birds, and it continued.

Gene Clifton is our Trust Membership Secretary. She was appointed in 1982, and has been with the Trust almost as long as me. Gene was my right arm during the period when birds were brought to The Wick to be saved, and the two of us carried the brunt of the feeding and cleaning up. We learned the proper way to get food into birds that wouldn't eat, and how to handle them. We enjoyed the elation of seeing a bird take to the air again, and felt sadness if it died on us. It would have been impossible without Gene, and I am very grateful to her. Vicki Gladwyn also gave a welcome hand with the casualties, and so did my

son Jonathan, who helped keep the log of all the case histories. Word had got around that The Wick was taking in injured birds. Faced with a child carrying a box, we had no choice.

Most of the casualties were medium to large birds, which are easy to see if they are grounded. There were ten adult kestrels, eight tawny owls, four little owls, two barn owls, and even one of the long-eared owls that nested at The Wick, plus moorhens, mallards, various gulls, several rooks and jackdaws. Gina found herself mum to an entire brood of orphan kestrel chicks. Although very young, the family knew instinctively how to protect itself. Whenever she fed them in their box, they rolled onto their backs and Gina was then faced with twelve feet, each tipped with needle-sharp talons. She raised all six.

If there was one thing we were wary of, it was fish-eating birds with long necks with a dagger on the end. Herons, divers and grebes need to be handled very carefully, especially if you are trying to push a fish down the throat. I think it was the fish-eating birds that we all remember most, because they could create wholesale dismay and consternation all round by simultaneously squirting from one end and projectile-vomiting from the other.

1983 was remarkable, because three different birds arrived within a month that are still talked about today. The first two were tawny owlets, which grew into adults we named Big Wol and Little Wol. After being released, they stayed together as adults and often perched in the garden at dusk and hooted and called to us for food. The other was a young female kestrel we called Kes. She had been taken from the nest as a chick and was very tame when she came to us. Kes mated with a wild kestrel and produced two families. Her party trick was to hover above, and then swoop down to catch food thrown into the air whilst the visitors clicked their cameras.

The Trust had grown in influence, in membership, in staff, in professional ability, and in internal complexity. By the early 1980s it was also a major landowner in the county. Looking into the crystal ball it was clear that the Trust must continue to grow to meet the challenges and threats to the countryside which have become ever more serious. Chairman Don Hunford was emphatic that the Trust needed a good man at the helm to achieve all this, and in 1987 John Hall, our Conservation Officer was appointed to the post of Trust Director. Although the Visitor Centre had been our *de facto* HQ since 1975, it was John who actually elevated it to a real HQ worthy of the Trust. Other key staff were Trust secretary Val Crookes and assistant secretary Gill Thompson. A dramatic early test of the quality of our new Director came in the form of the once-in-a-lifetime storm that ripped through our reserves in October 1987. Most of the woodland reserves became unsafe places to visit, and it needed good organisation at the top to get the situation under control.

At the height of the storm Gina and I stood at the windows to watch the spectacle. At 2.00 am, the horizon was illuminated by the constant flashes of electricity substations and pylon cables under extreme duress. We could see the giant willow beside the lake was fighting for its life. Come morning, the tree stood, but four bird hides had been destroyed. We were lucky.

The scarce emerald damselfy is colonising the reserve. In the 1980s it was near extinction in Britain.
Photograph: Ted Benton.

Chapter 9

Brent goose odyssey

The dark-bellied brent geese we see in autumn and winter from our bird hides at The Wick are Siberians, born and bred. After enjoying our mild winter, they go home to breed. Let's follow the first flock of birds to leave.

Made restive by the longer daylight hours and rising temperatures of early spring, a flock of 200 geese stop grazing the short vegetation on the Geedon salt marsh next to Fingringhoe Wick. Roughly one-third are juveniles, and the rest are mature adults. In the gathering dusk one evening in early March, the lights of Brightlingsea seem close. Suddenly, five adult geese and then 50 and then the whole flock is in flight. Skimming low over the mudflats, the geese see the last of the safe and secure refuge where for thousands of years birds from the Arctic have spent winter. Four of these long-lived birds first saw the Colne estuary fifteen years ago, and have spent every winter of their lives here.

Beating low over the sea to get 'lift' from the waves, the geese move steadily along the Suffolk coast. Perhaps using the sharp stab of light from the Southwold lighthouse as a marker, they swing east and stream out across the North Sea in two wide, shallow 'V' formations. Migrating

wildfowl conserve energy by flying in this manner. Apart from the bird at the tip of the arrow, every bird flies in the slipstream of the bird in front: it creates extra lift, and the bird uses less energy in maintaining speed and keeping station in the formation. Conserving energy on a journey of 3000 miles is a life or death matter. Taking turns, older, experienced birds that have made the journey several times have the punishing job of leading the formation.

Birds on migration usually fly by night, and spend the day resting and feeding. The older geese have the route in their minds, and they also know the safe and remote places where feeding is good. Daylight finds the flock on the coastal island of Texel, in the Netherlands. The island is one of a chain enclosing the Waddenzee – a shallow, enclosed sea where the feeding is good. The flock lingers here until early May, and is joined by thousands of other brents for whom the area is a vital migration staging post. Moving along the coast, our flock stay for several days on the salt marshes at the mouth of the river Elbe, in Germany. The geese make leisurely progress, seeking marshlands, river deltas, coastal islands and farmland where they can feed and rest during the day. Soon, they are in the flat farm

Dark-bellied brent geese. *Photograph: Bob Glover*

fields of Denmark, where they spend ten days. Overstaying their welcome, three geese are killed by a farmer protecting his crops.

So far, the weather has been in their favour, but crossing the Baltic the flock runs into a severe gale and heavy snow: 20 juvenile geese do not have the strength to keep up, and they fall out of the formations. The rest are forced down onto the island of Gotland. The feeding is poor, and when the snow stops after dark the geese are on their way again. In Estonia coastal marshland attracts the hungry brents, and they stay several days: there is no need to hurry – instinct and experience of their savage homeland has taught them

that Siberia is no use to them as a breeding ground until well into June. There are hundreds more brent geese in the boggy grassland, and when our flock eventually moves on, it has swelled to nearly 500 birds. After crossing the Gulf of Finland, the flock passes over a land forested with birch, and strewn with ice age lakes. Passing within sight of the lights of Archangel the flock enters western Russia, the halfway point on its epic journey. Two hundred miles further north-east, and the brents cross the Arctic Circle into the tundra, their true home. Fifteen hundred miles to go.

The Arctic ocean is fringed by coastal tundra. It encircles the ocean from Norway eastwards through Lapland,

Russia, Asia, the United States and Canada. Night after night, the brents pass over a land of permafrost that stretches from horizon to horizon: soon, the rock-hard terrain will thaw as the Arctic spring arrives at last, and then the tundra will become a waterlogged morass. Siberia: a land barely out of the ice age, where immense north-flowing rivers – Yenisey, Lena, Ob – empty into the Arctic ocean in a confusion of delta islands, peninsulas and marshlands. The brent geese are almost home, but they are too early. Spring is late this year, and the land is still locked in ice. They are forced to find what food they can, where they can, on offshore coastal islands where the snow is patchy and showing areas of green vegetation, and at the water's edge along the banks of rivers and creeks. This is a bad time for the brents, and many die. The Arctic spring slowly creeps north, and at last the flock takes to the air for the final stage of their migration to the bleak and wonderful place where they were all born – the Taimyr Peninsula. Fewer than half the geese that began the journey are there at its end. The losses are high, but the birds that survived are the strongest, fittest and most adaptable. Their offspring will inherit these traits.

Taimyr is one of the most hostile environments on Earth. Hundreds of miles inside the Arctic Circle, its coastline is sheathed in sea ice. In the very brief summer, sixteen mammal species migrate there to breed, including musk ox, polar bear, lemming and 500,000 reindeer. With continuous daylight, the immense wilderness is a magnet for over 50 bird species that nest in the tussocky sedges, or on rocky cliffs. Myriad meltwater pools hatch teeming insects to feed the young birds in the nests. The brent geese will share their tundra breeding grounds with red-breasted geese, knot, golden plover, long-tailed skua, snowy owl and many more. There are no trees, and all these ground-nesting birds must live with the daily threat from the Arctic fox.

The summer lasts just two months, and brings the flowering of the glacier buttercup, Arctic poppy, alpine dryas, purple saxifrage, the grasses and the sedges. August however, brings the first frosts. It is a signal to the indefatigable brents that very soon they must leave and take their young far away from the killing Arctic cold. Soon, Taimyr will lose the sun for months on end. In the howling darkness the tundra will be empty of life, and the ice age will once more grip the land.

Photograph: Chris Gibson

Chapter 10

Forty years of wildlife conservation

The Trust celebrated its 40th birthday in 1999, and two years later it was the turn of The Wick. A lot of tides have ebbed and flowed since the old gravel workings became a nature reserve, and many exciting things have happened. One of the most satisfying from my viewpoint was the official designation in 1989 of the Colne Estuary as a Site of Special Scientific Interest – with Fingringhoe Wick included in the SSSI area. Nationally, hundreds of such sites protect the full range of the UK's natural and near-natural habitats, as well as native species and geological features. They are the jewels in our crown.

By then, Fred Boot had been Chairman of the Trust for four years. Very few people can hold a candle to Fred for enthusiasm, energy and sheer ability in committee work and administration. The Trust was enhanced by the years of Fred's chairmanship. The nature reserve also benefited, because for a long time he was also Chairman of the management committee for the reserve and the Visitor Centre.

Ever aware of its responsibility to Essex wildlife in the future, each of our Visitor Centres has a staff Education Officer. Martin Rapley was our Education Officer for many years, with a talent for getting the message over to children that was instinctive and highly successful. Laura Hopkins is another 'natural'. She was appointed in 2004 and quickly became popular with her school groups.

The third member of the core team of three staff at each Centre is the Centre Manager. Succeeding Jeanette Forder and Sue Foster, Janet Hulse was appointed to the post in 2002. Janet has veterinary experience, and I often think how much Gene and I needed someone like her when we struggled to cope with the bird casualties in the 1980s. Jenny Rolfe became Centre Manager in 2004. She too has an ability to attract volunteers to the Centre, and to make them feel very much appreciated. Yes, it sounds obvious, but it is surprising how often volunteers are taken for granted. Arnold Beardwell was a volunteer in the Centre just a couple of years after it opened in 1975. He was a veteran before I even arrived on the scene, and he and his friend Bob Jennings have helped to maintain the Centre for years. We owe them a lot.

A changing climate

If there is one thing we can be sure of after years of forecasting and doom and gloom from experts, it is that we do not know if current warmer temperatures and extreme weather are evidence of The Big One – irreversible global warming. Sea level is certainly rising, and in a low-lying county like Essex its impact on both people and wildlife could be great. Experimental management on coastal realignment at the Trust's Abbotts Hall Farm site on the Blackwater estuary will provide important knowledge that could create new coastal wildlife habitats, but it is difficult to foretell the effect on salt marshes in the Colne estuary if they are submerged by more frequent high tides than in past centuries. Wildlife is highly responsive to a changing environment – witness all the losses and gains in species at The Wick in recent decades. Little egrets are now a daily sighting on the salt marshes, and these elegant small herons from the continent are now nesting in Essex. A small wasp – the bee wolf – from southern Europe is now well established in the reserve, and indeed in many counties farther north. A wasp and a fish-eating bird are extremes, but they indicate that wildlife is on the move: from the continent to Britain, from southern Britain to the north, and from low ground to high ground. Many species will find a suitable new environment; the losers will not.

The flora and fauna of Fingringhoe Wick has always been a changing feast, and whether for reasons of habitat deterioration, our management, or a warming – or cooling – climate, it will continue to change.

The return of the machines: 1987–2005

No matter how hard the volunteers and I worked to maintain the diversity of wildlife habitats at The Wick, it

was obvious we had been beaten by the scale and the speed of natural succession that turned bare ground into woodland in just 40 years. The original gravel pit features were all but gone by 1987, and rampant scrub and woodland was encroaching on every terrestrial habitat except the salt marsh. To maintain the richness of habitats, and to ensure that non-woodland species had a future in the nature reserve some important decisions were made. Starting that very year, the machines that had first created the gravel pit were brought back. Not the actual machines – but their 1980s' descendants, with enormous power and versatility. It was also decided that the oak must be controlled: although a fine tree of great benefit to hundreds of species, the proliferation of the oak will result in the loss of the thickets, and the whole character of The Wick and its wildlife will be changed. Both decisions are proving very effective, and both are now priority items in the Management Plan. Because The Wick is a Site of Special Scientific Interest, all management proposals must have the consent of English Nature. For many years I have enjoyed the enthusiastic support of Chris Gibson, Senior Conservation Officer at English Nature in Colchester. Chris is an inspiring, all-round naturalist with a particular talent for the down-to-earth, practical advice all wardens seek.

In the expert hands of someone like Jack Webb, a 22-ton excavator

East Heath in 2003

Above: With the aid of a bulldozer, the soil is scraped to benefit the flora and invertebrates.

Below: The East Heath following scrub removal and scraping. The bare slopes, pond and disturbed soil re-create conditions that were abundant in 1961.

is a precision tool that can exert terrifying power one moment, and great delicacy the next. Jack works for Hugh Pearl (Drainage) Ltd., one of the Trust's Corporate Partners. With the guidance and experience of Pearl's Peter Sloman, several projects have been carried out with excellent results. The ecological clock has been running for over 40 years, and the idea is to select areas where we will re-set it back to the beginning. We can do this by removing and burying scrub, and by scraping away the topsoil to expose the underlying sand and gravel. At the same time, we can re-create a typical suite of features that were once common in the old pit: shallow ponds, spoil heaps, spreads of sand, small cliffs and disturbed ground. In effect, we can make small, brand-new pits within the surrounding older pit. This rejuvenation of selected sites produces startling results very quickly, especially in the gravel pit wild flowers which rapidly colonise the bare ground exactly as they first did in 1959.

Fingringhoe Wick in 2004

Following decades of Trust management, the condition of the habitats may be summarised in this snapshot impression. Woodland: *flourishing*. Scrub: *good*. Ponds: *good, if rainfall ok. More ponds needed.* Lake: *visually stunning and a great centre-piece, but of low value to wildfowl.* Salt marsh: *in good shape, but receding.* Grassland: *good, thanks to rabbits and to our annual management.* Bare and disturbed ground: *excellent new habitats created in 2003/4. More needed.* The Scrape: *poor and deteriorating. It will be allowed to become a reedbed.* Reedbeds: *declining and being invaded by scrub.* Heathland: *good, thanks to grazing by rabbits.*

For some of the key wildlife species a similar report would be as follows. Nightingales: *widespread, stable breeding population.* Kingfisher: *no longer nesting.* Turtle dove: *about seven breeding pairs.* Badger: *flourishing.* Water vole: *occasionally seen in Kit's pond.* Adder: *numerous.* Great crested newt: *present in many of the older ponds.* Great silver beetle: *present in Kit's pond.* Green hairstreak: *very cyclical.* Hairy dragonfly: *breeding in two ponds.* Sparrowhawk: *a regular breeder.* Common spotted orchid: *in serious decline.* Hornet: *numerous colonies.*

These are a few of the popular, high-profile wildlife species that visitors ask about and hope to see. We try, however, to keep track of the fortunes of as many others as we can. There are well over 2000 species that we know of, and very probably a similar number – mainly invertebrates – that we have yet to discover. A major purpose of this book is to record our current knowledge of The Wick and its wildlife. Many years into the future it should be possible for people to use the book as a benchmarker and say, *in 2004, this is how it was.* In the following pages, expert amateur naturalists familiar with the reserve, have contributed many reports that embrace most of the wildlife. The reports are followed by species lists as an appendix.

You may find the next section the best part of the book – or you may not. It is a summary of what we know. Please read it, because it is an inventory of the wildlife of The Wick, and it puts various habitats and current management under the microscope and touches on what the future might hold for some species affected by climate change.

Many of the following contributors are members of Colchester Natural History Society. Before we came to

The Wick, Gina and I were active members of CNHS, and we have rich and numerous memories of field trips all over East Anglia. We are members still. The society is living proof of the important role that expert amateur naturalists play in the Essex countryside of the 21st century. CNHS, which celebrated its 50th anniversary in 2004, records wildlife in north-east Essex. Thankfully, The Wick lies in its manor.

One year after scraping the shoreline of the lake, many different plant species are colonising the bare ground.

Memory Lane

The old gravel workings were a blank canvas in the early 1960s. Without doubt, they would eventually support a rich variety of wildlife, but our awareness of the flora and fauna at the time depended upon individuals being prepared to scramble and slide in the chaotic terrain in search of yet more species to add to our knowledge. Colchester Natural History Society was very prominent in those early investigations, and indeed was also a key local supporter of the campaign by the then Essex Naturalists' Trust to buy the old pit. Joe Firmin is the President of CNHS, and also chairman of the Essex Moth Group. I am grateful to him for the following snapshot account of recording at The Wick which spanned three decades.

A memoir

Botanists and entomologists in Colchester Natural History Society's specialist survey groups provided most of the early records resulting from early surveys after the acquisition of The Wick. The use of mercury-vapour lamps powered by portable generators led to a number of interesting discoveries of localised moth species, especially in the salt marsh and reedbed areas. It was found that there was a flourishing colony of the beautiful and exotic-looking cream-spot tiger moth, and that the reedbed held a population of Webb's wainscot moth. Also recorded were salt marsh specialities such as

rosy wave, ground lackey, dog's tooth and dotted fanfoot. Jerry Heath and the late, much-missed Fred Buck and I were regularly in action with the moth traps in the late 1960s, the 1970s and early 1980s.

A summer night in the 1970s must be recorded for posterity. The plan was for the recording team, on this occasion joined by the late David Rowston, CNHS chairman, to take their very heavy generator to the edge of the reedbed and set up the mercury-vapour lamp on a pole, with a sheet underneath for the moths to alight on. All went well when the lamp was lit after 10 pm, and there were good arrivals on the sheet, including Webb's wainscot, the local speciality. Then disaster struck. David Rowston, who hadn't been 'mothing' for years and was very excited, suddenly spied a cream-spot tiger spiralling in toward the MV lamp. He had brought his ancient butterfly net on a long pole, and couldn't resist a swipe at the exotic arrival. Unfortunately, the years had taken their toll of David's netmanship skills. The lunge hit the precious MV lamp and all was darkness and expletives.

In those days we didn't have a spare MV bulb, so the disconsolate party made its way back to the Bunkhouse. Turning on the light, David said: *'I know how I can make amends chaps. I've brought a bottle of whisky in case the night gets cold. Let's enjoy that, open the Bunkhouse window and see what moths find their way in.'* So the time to midnight passed ever convivially. History has it that there was a total of more than 50 species, but maybe there was a degree of double vision that night! And yes, the party had well and truly sobered up by the time of departure in the wee small hours.

Joe Firmin

Bare sand and clay is soon hidden by a rampant growth of plant colonisers.

Wildlife reports

RDB 1? Noteable A?

When you read the following wildlife reports you will come across a few mystifying things like the above. They are references to Red Data Books. Adrian Knowles is Senior Ecologist for the Trust's Essex Ecology Services offshoot: he explains what it all means.

The overriding aim of Red Data Books is to draw attention to those species whose continued survival is threatened in the area under scrutiny. The first lists were promoted by the International Union for the Conservation of Nature (IUCN), and were generally global lists of the most endangered plants and animals. In more recent years, national and even county Red Data lists are being produced to highlight the plight of our flora and fauna. It should be remembered that listing in a Red Data Book is an indication of how *threatened or endangered* a species is, not how *rare* it is, although the two factors are generally closely related. The critical difference is that even a quite locally widespread species in terms of 'dots on a map' can be highly threatened if it has very precise habitat requirements, with all its sites being in an unfavourable or fragile condition. An example would be a water snail that needs very pure water: it would be universally threatened because of pollution or agricultural chemical run-off. It should also be remembered that Red Data Book listing confers no degree of legal protection – it is merely a 'Domesday' catalogue of those species that may become extinct locally, nationally or globally unless positive conservation action is taken.

Adrian Knowles

Water vole: threatened, endangered – or just rare?
Courtesy English Nature

Mammals

A visitor to The Wick may quite easily see 60 bird species on a good day. It would be unusual to see eight mammal species. Without doubt however, the group as a whole has grown in diversity as the old gravel workings slowly changed to thickets, scrub, woodland and grassland. In 2004 it is likely that seventeen species are present.

The brown hare was once common in surrounding fields but is now rare. It is sometimes seen on the reserve, although it does not breed. The house mouse is trapped very occasionally in the house, but not in the Centre. It was once present in the Bunkhouse and Tin Shed, and may well now be extinct at The Wick. The brown rat makes seasonal assaults on the Centre in the autumn and winter and attacks the bags of rubbish. It does not breed on the reserve.

The harvest mouse is elusive, and I do not think a live animal has ever been seen. It seems to be established in reedy areas, where the summer nests have been found. Several were discovered in the Boathouse Pond reeds in 1977, and occasional carcases have also been found. A summer nest was found in 1998 in long grass next to Kit's pond, and another on the old lake island in 1999. A Longworth trap survey in 1963 revealed the wood mouse to be widespread and common, and this was borne out in subsequent surveys in 1977 and 1979. In contrast, the yellow-necked mouse was thought to be absent in 1977. However, a dead specimen was identified by David Corke in 1979, and up to 2004 almost every mouse trapped in the house and Centre was a yellow-neck. A description in 1983 of an animal that could only have been a dormouse has bugged me ever since. A survey in 2003 was negative, but the search goes on. The rabbit is abundant in the nature reserve and surrounding fields. The non-stop grazing controls scrub, and their scuffling and digging creates the disturbed soil conditions that benefit many insect and flower species. In late summer there is a small outbreak of myxomatosis that kills a few annually.

A large area of the northern edge of the reserve was never excavated: the Wick Farm soil still lies deep, rich and full of earthworms. The mole is common in the unexcavated area, and the characteristic hills are abundant in some years. In a short spell of really hot summer weather, it is not unusual to find several dead moles on the nature trails: presumably, if earthworms are hard to locate for even a short time, it can be fatal for the mole. Snowfall reveals the tiny footprints of nocturnal small mammals. Voles, shrews and mice have passed this way, although their identities can only be revealed by licensed live-trapping surveys and analysis of owl pellets. The common shrew and pygmy shrew are sometimes found dead on the paths, and there have been several live sightings of the water shrew in ponds in the late 1990s, including one seen by Jonathan Forsyth in the garden pond in 1995.

The Small Mammals surveys of 1963 and 1977 established that the field vole was common and widespread in grassland, especially the old grazing meadow on the north boundary. The bank vole was also found to be common in similar areas, and one was found in the house in 1999. Despite the ponds and the lake, the water vole has always been a rarity. Occasionally one or two have been seen in Kit's pond, but it is likely they overspill into the reserve from the adjacent long, reedy borrow-dyke when the population climbs.

Records of stoat and weasel go back to the early 1960s. Both animals can easily be seen by visitors in the daytime, and consequently there are steady reports in the spring and summer. The predation of a family of young kingfishers in their nest burrow was the work of a weasel. With the steady development of woodland across the old gravel workings, the badger has become a welcome resident. Earliest records are of tracks in 1972, and from then on badgers regularly came to forage on the reserve. Exploratory setts were noticed in 1993, and the following year four cubs were seen. Since then, numerous setts have been opened up. In 2005 badger roads, latrine pits, tracks and feeding signs are a common sight in most areas.

Ever alert to the possibility of a snack, badgers turn up at dusk to eat fallen greengages and apples in the garden.

The fox is common and widespread in the countryside around the reserve, but the barren gravel workings were probably unsuitable in the early days. There are several pairs living and breeding at The Wick, and their tracks, droppings and territorial musking sites are daily observations. The arrival of woodland also saw the arrival of other woodland mammals. The grey squirrel was first recorded in 1979, and is now common. Muntjac deer were also first recorded in that year – but not again until 1981. Another was seen in 1999. In 2002, an adult and a fawn were seen and they are now resident.

Pipistrelle bats – possibly living in the house loft – are seen at dusk in spring and summer when they emerge to feed.

Laurie Forsyth

Fox. *Courtesy English Nature.*

Birds

The bird population at The Wick has changed through the decades in response to their changing habitats, and to external factors such as intensive farming. Perhaps the best way to tell the story is to choose three periods in the history of the reserve, and to begin each with a description of the changing reserve at that time. The following report covers just species seen in the reserve itself, not birds in the surrounding landscape.

1961–1976

The Wick in the early years of this period was mainly bare gravel workings dominated by the lake and numerous ponds. There were scattered thickets, fragments of farm hedges, a reedbed, and an old pasture and willow woodland on the north boundary. Extensive scrub, gorse heath and grassland came later, as did the man-made plantation and the Scrape.

The lake was the magnet for many birds at the time: there was no woodland, and the open aspect attracted traditional gravel pit species like mallard and other common water birds. Three pairs of kingfishers nested, and the sand martins flourished nearby in their nest cliff. Between 1969 and 1971 the lake – and the food it contained – brought occasional rarities such as purple heron, little bittern, bittern,

garganey, scaup, smew and osprey. One pair of great crested grebe nested in the mid-1970s, and one pair of mute swan nested almost every year.

Several pairs of nesting skylark are testimony to how open The Wick was, even in 1969. Willow carr-like woodland formed much of the old boundary on the northern side, and this attracted nesting tree creeper, willow tit, spotted flycatcher and lesser spotted woodpecker. All are now long gone. Developing scrub and the dense young plantation held four pairs of nesting grasshopper warbler in the early 1970s. The reedbed and lake edge held about 20 pairs of nesting reed warbler, and a dozen pairs of sedge warbler. The gorse heath habitat supported over 20 pairs of yellowhammer and 30 pairs of linnet. The fire in 1972 hit both species. Both recovered well to pre-fire numbers by 1976. Thickets concealed about fifteen pairs of nightingale each spring. Other breeding birds at the time include goldcrest and lesser redpoll and, in 1962, a pair of meadow pipit.

Winter visitors included occasional shore lark on the beach, bearded tit in the reeds, twite, which drank from puddles in the road, and flocks of redwing and fieldfare. A mixed flock of these Scandinavian thrushes roosted each night in the plantation in 1973 and was estimated to number 12,000 birds. Red-backed shrike occurred annually between 1970 and 1977. A stone curlew dropped into the dry Scrape in 1976.

1977–1990

Extensive thickets and scrub by now covered the old gravel workings. Permanent ponds had declined to three, and the lake and Trout Pool were surrounded by trees. The plantation was dominated by tall pines. Elm on the north boundary died from disease and the Scrape was at its best.

Turtle dove peaked at 20 pairs in 1977. Long-eared owl used a winter roost at Kit's pond for many years, and then a single pair nested intermittently from 1983 up to 1999. Tawny owl began breeding in the same period.

The Scrape, which Stewart Linsell created was at its most productive in 1978: Malcolm Wright counted 120 redshank, and many spotted redshank, plus greenshank, green sandpiper and lapwing all feeding at the same time. I claim the record however for the number of species present simultaneously in the Scrape: seventeen in August 1987, comprising waders, shorebirds and wildfowl. A pair of water rail raised six chicks there in 1998. Ringed plover nested successfully on the upper beach in 1979. Cetti's warbler – always predicted as a breeding bird – was

Tufted duck *(left)*, ruddy duck *(below)* and pochard *(below left)* breed on the lake each year. These diving duck are noticeably more successful than the surface-feeding mallard. Shoveler *(right)* occasionally breed successfully in the Scrape. *Photographs: David Harrison.*

heard singing in 1985, but has never nested. A family of crossbill stripping cones in the plantation in 1988 raised false hopes of breeding, but they were outsiders looking for a meal. A night heron astonished watchers at the lake in 1983.

1990–2004

Extensive work on the lake thrust back the woodland to make it more attractive for wildfowl. For the first time, mechanical clearance of old scrub was adopted as a method of management which is now regarded as highly successful. Open areas were enlarged, new ponds were made and grassland and heathland sites were improved by using special equipment.

Despite the quality of their habitats on the reserve, it was not enough to save the yellowhammer, linnet and reed bunting: their numbers plunged, and then they were gone, along with other farmland species in the surrounding countryside. The mixed woodland attracted our first nesting pairs of sparrowhawk, magpie and carrion crow. Meanwhile, in the thickets the nightingale went from strength to strength, and by May 2000 it is my personal belief there were 40 males present. Bullfinch numbers have always been low, but stable. Turtle dove declined to about four pairs in 2002. One pair of little owl nested in the same year. Oddly, and against the national trend, blackbird, song thrush and mistle thrush all increased.

Pochard, tufted duck, dabchick, ruddy duck and mute swan regularly nested on the lake, and in 2001 a pair of oystercatchers nested in the Scrape. A rarity occurred in the form of a singing male marsh warbler in 1999. Blackcap, whitethroat, lesser whitethroat, reed warbler, garden warbler and chiffchaff are regular breeders. Wren and chaffinch numbers are increasing. Marsh harrier now regularly nest close to the reserve, and visitors see them beating low over our reedy areas trying to flush out coots and moorhens.

I wish to thank all the observers who have contributed their sightings over the years, and especially Geoff Boyle for his annual breeding birds survey, and Nigel Cuming and Ruth Tucker for the monthly wildfowl and wader counts.

Laurie Forsyth

Reptiles and amphibians

When a gravel pit closes down and nothing is done to restore the landscape, wildlife moves swiftly to stake its claim. All those hectares of sunny, eroding spoil heaps and the boggy bits around the many ponds were fine places in the 1960s for adders, grass snakes, slow worms and newts, and they have probably been present from the earliest days of the reserve.

The large and handsome great crested newt has been recorded many times at The Wick. This is an important animal, and listed as a Biodiversity Action Plan species requiring special consideration and conservation measures. Management work in and around ponds can be damaging to the newt, and great care is taken when improving an old pond, in creating a new one, or in managing thickets within 500 m of a pond, because the newts are probably hibernating in the woodland. The tadpole with its distinctive gills is often found in ponds by our Education Officer when pond-dipping with school groups, and adults hibernating beneath logs are a regular sight to volunteers in working parties in winter. Smooth newts are much more common.

Surprisingly, the common frog is probably not present. For many years,

the public brought spawn, froglets and adult frogs to The Wick to release in the ponds. The practice ceased long ago when redleg disease made it dangerous, and when it also became apparent that despite all the water, the bulk of the reserve will suddenly become arid in summer and hostile to young froglets just out of the ponds. The common toad existed in one tiny population in the shallow end of the lake, and another at Kit's pond. Tiny toadlets were found in 2002.

The slow worm and the common lizard are only occasionally seen, and possibly both are more common than we think. As a matter of course, chunks of masonry, bricks and logs are left in sunny places to attract these and our other reptiles: they all need to bask. The run of mild winters that began in the mid-1990s has benefited them, and the adder in particular has become widespread. Our management policy of scraping away scrub and topsoil to expose bare ground and create shallow ponds will produce the sort of terrain that will benefit adders and also grass snakes that bask at the edge of the new ponds, and feed on aquatic life.

Laurie Forsyth

The ponds and their aquatic invertebrates

The mirror-surface of ponds reveal little of what's going on down below. They swarm with life, as proved by school pond-dipping forays. Ponds, pools, puddles and the lake are all different environments for the creatures that live in them, and as a result the variety of species is great. Pam and Peter Wilson specialise in the study of aquatic life, and I appreciate the time and effort they have spent in surveying The Wick's ponds that has resulted in the following report.

Over 160 invertebrate species were identified during pond surveys in the spring and summer of 2004 – a very good number for a relatively small site. The list includes: flatworms (3 species), leeches (4), water snails and pea mussels (16), crustaceans (7), nymphs of dragonflies and damselflies (16), mayfly nymphs (2), aquatic bugs (29), aquatic beetles (65), alderfly larvae (1), caddis fly larvae (12), mosquito larvae (8) and larvae of soldier flies (2).

Many of the species are characteristic of coastal areas. Obvious examples are found in the brackish water of Kit's pond and the Scrape. A prawn, *Palaemonetes varians* and a brackish water shrimp, *Gammarus zaddachi* were found in both, but a mud snail, *Ventrosia ventrosa*, which is a Biodiversity Action Plan (BAP) species was only in the Scrape. These are brackish water species and absent from the other ponds. However, some species which normally live in brackish water can survive in fresh water: a lesser water boatman, *Sigara stagnalis* and the scarce beetles *Agabus conspersus* and *Enochrus halophilus* turned up in several fresh water ponds. Conversely, some predominantly fresh water species will tolerate brackish water and live in Kit's pond and the Scrape. The scarce beetles *Limnoxenus niger* and *Rhantus frontalis* rarely occur inland.

Unexpectedly, a population of the local water bug *Mesovelia furcata* was found in Kit's pond, with a smaller number of juveniles in the Scrape. Previously, we have found single specimens only, from two fresh water ponds in the Colchester area.

Most of the ponds at The Wick are slightly acid. As a result some of the species are characteristic of acid or heathland pools such as the scarce beetles *Agabus chalconatus* and *Hydrochus angustatus*. Like some of the coastal species, they are widely distributed throughout the reserve. In contrast, the old farm pond that is fed by a spring close to the northern boundary of the reserve is not acid: *Anisus leucostoma,* a snail that has some preference for hard water was found here. Another species of interest in the pond is the water beetle *Hydroporus discretus*, which is often associated with springs. This pond is one of two where *Graptodytes bilineatus,* a rare (RDB 3) water beetle was found in April 2004: nymphs of the scarce emerald damselfly *Lestes dryas* (RDB 2) were found in July 2004. The latter was also found in Pine pond. Both species are coastal.

Shady pools in hollows support species typical of this habitat, such as the beetles *Hydroporus memnonius* (which is local) and *Suphrodytes dorsalis* which were rarely found elsewhere on the reserve. The larva of the caddis *Holocentropus stagnalis* and certain mosquitoes also seem to favour these areas. Other species are confined mainly to winter-wet ponds, such as the snail *Lymnaea truncatula* and the larva of the caddis *Limnephilus auricula.*

Newly created ponds may look barren and unfriendly to wildlife, but they are yet another specialised habitat and are quickly colonised by plants and animals. The scarce beetle *Hydroglyphus pusillis* is a coloniser of new ponds. In 2004 it was found in two ponds created in November 2003, together with a large number of nymphs of the broad-bodied chaser dragonfly *Libellula depressa.* Other species were present – water beetles and bugs will fly from one pond to another – including the water bug *Sigara nigrolineata* and the only specimen of the beetle *Laccophilous hyalinus* we have seen, although nationally it is common.

The lake has more species than any other pond at The Wick, because of its size and complexity. An exciting find here is the scarce water snail *Gyraulus laevis,* which is only the second recent record for north Essex. The nymphs of many dragonflies are present, including those of the scarce hairy dragonfly *Brachytron pratense.* A tiny lesser water boatman, *Cymatia coleoptrata* (local) seems to prefer larger ponds: it is common here although it is unusual in the Colchester area. The dramatically large and strange-looking water stick insect *Ranatra linearis* is also present, and it too seems to prefer large ponds. Larvae and pupae of the unusual mosquito *Coquilletetidia richiardia* are adapted to pierce aquatic plants and breath air from their air-spaces, and they occur in good numbers at the western end of the lake, although nowhere else on the reserve. Like most of the mosquitoes at The Wick, the adult female bites people.

This report offers just a glimpse of the aquatic invertebrates on the nature reserve: there is much more to learn from this fascinating site.

Pam and Peter Wilson

Great diving beetle.
Courtesy English Nature.

Molluscs:
Snails and slugs

Bird watchers in the estuary hides at low water are often mystified by the spectacle of dozens of shelducks apparently slurping liquid mud as they methodically work their way across the glistening ooze. In reality, the ducks are efficiently hoovering up vast numbers of one of their favourite foods: snails. Researchers calculate that the surface mud in a single square metre can support up to 10,000 tiny, grazing spire shells. John Llewellyn-Jones is a mollusc expert: they are few and far between, and I am very pleased he has carried out snail and slug surveys to produce the following account.

Fingringhoe Wick became a nature reserve after 40 years of gravel extraction. The barren moonscape eventually became vegetated, with a variety of habitats that included bare gravel, open areas of grass and invading herbs, gorse heathland, scrubland with hawthorn and bramble, mixed woodland and a conifer plantation. It also has a fresh-water stream, ponds and lakes as well as salt marsh, a beach, mudflats and some stable objects such as boulders and the jetty.

This range of habitats means that there should be a very wide range of molluscs. There are two limitations however for the mollusc species that have colonised The Wick. Firstly, there is a lack of lime or chalk, and secondly, the reserve tends to rapidly dry out. Species present are those that do not need a lot of calcium carbonate for shell making and those that can cope with periods of drought.

No live molluscs were found on the open gravel and sand. A few species were found in the open grassy areas, but most were found under scrub or in woodland. An account of some of the fresh-water mollusc species at The Wick is found in Pam and Peter Wilson's report on aquatic fauna, elsewhere in this book. Because salt marsh and estuarine conditions are very variable there are only a few mollusc species present, although they are well adapted to these conditions.

Starting with the terrestrial molluscs, the smallest found on the reserve was the 1 mm-long, pure white, short-toothed herald snail *Carychium minimum*, found on a grassy/mossy bank and also in damp leaf mould covered by a layer of moss in mixed woodland. An interesting mollusc found living in the cracks of the bark of hawthorn trees was the brown, club-shaped, two-toothed door snail *Clausilia bidentata*, 1 cm long, which is one of the few species in Britain that has a left-handed spire. Two typical and common molluscs found on the reserve are the 2.5–5 mm discoidal, flattened-shelled garlic glass snail *Oxychilus alliarius* and the cellar glass snail *Oxychilus cellarius*. *O. alliarius* gives off a garlic smell when the animal is irritated while *O. cellarius* is found almost anywhere including cellars! They both have thin translucent shells with almost no calcium carbonate in them. The common garden snail *Helix aspersa* is the largest on the reserve, although it is not common. It has a 35 mm brown, yellow and white speckled shell. This snail, and also the brown-lipped or grove snail *Cepaea nemoralis*, a yellow, through pink to brown snail, 20 mm, with up to five dark bands and a brown lip, and also the white-lipped snail *C. hortensis*, having a similarly coloured shell, 15 mm long, with a white lip, are both reasonably common. All three species produce claspers, known as 'love darts' during copulation which are a different shape for each species and can therefore be used to identify them. A number of thrush anvils were found with the broken shells of *Cepaea nemoralis* and *C. hortensis*. There are only a few slugs because the habitats become too dry.

The salt marsh is a very difficult habitat to adapt to, and only a few species are present. Mouse-ear shelled snail *Ovatella (Phytia) myosotis*, 8 mm long, is a brown, translucent, primitive-lunged pulmonate. It is particularly interesting in that the internal whorl walls are dissolved away to make a single compartment to make room for the animal's growth. The dun sentinel *Assiminea grayana* is a tubby snail of 5 mm, which has a horny door to close off the shell from the outside. It was recorded by Jeffreys in 1869 from 'the banks of the Thames, between Greenwich and a little below Gravesend, mostly above ordinary high water mark'. Since then it has spread from the Thames estuary at least as far as Fingringhoe Wick. The third species is the laver spire shell *Hydrobia ulvae*, which is a horny-coloured, opaque snail, 5 mm, found in immense numbers feeding on sea lettuce *Ulva lactuca* or on the open mud. There are two seaslug species found living on *Vaucheria*, a green, moss-like salt marsh plant growing on the mud. One is *Alderia modesta*, a seaslug, 4 mm long, with approximately 26 greeny-yellow cerata on its back. The other is *Limapontia depressa*, a seaslug, 3 mm long, that is normally black. Both tend to be commonest during the winter months.

The seashore is also a mollusc habitat. There are three variations at The Wick: the sandy shore, the muddy shore and the boulders and jetty. The sand however is too high up the beach for any species to colonise. The mud supports a number of bivalve species that bury themselves, including *Scrobicularia plana*, *Cardium edule*, *Abra alba*, *A. tenuis*, *Mya arenaria* and *Macoma balthica*. The edible periwinkle *Littorina littorea* and the rough winkle *L. saxatilis* have a foothold on the stable boulders and jetty, which also support the blue edible mussel *Mytilus edulis*.

I would like to thank Dr Robert Cameron and Dr Adrian Rundle for their identifications.

John Llewellyn-Jones

Arachnida:
Pseudo-scorpions, harvestmen and spiders

Gina and I have lived with wildlife in the warden's house for 26 years. Pholcus spiders are ever-present in every room, every day of the year. As a warden I am embarrassed to admit that big spiders make me nervous. Keeping their distance, these daddy long-legs spiders creep along the ceilings and walls but certainly help to reduce the mosquito problem. A misty autumn morning at The Wick turns every single web to silver, and reveals the terrifying truth about the teeming numbers of spiders on the reserve. Ray Ruffell is a veteran stalwart of the reserve management team at The Wick, and spiders are his subject. Working with him on Sunday mornings has opened my eyes to spidery aspects of coppicing and scrub clearance, so that I have developed a guarded interest in them. Ray has kindly contributed information on which the following account of the spiders, harvestmen and the allied pseudo-scorpions has been based.

Pseudo-scorpions
Only two species have been recorded, both of which are common throughout Essex in a variety of habitats. They are *Chthonius ischnocheles* and *Neobisium carcinoides*.

Harvestmen
Of the 21 species recorded in Essex, seventeen have been found at The Wick. *Oligolophus hanseni* is regarded as rare in Essex. The single record for The Wick in 1971 was from a pitfall trap, but it is generally found as an adult in trees and bushes. Three species are regarded as scarce. Of these, *Opilio parietinus* is closely associated with man, *Paroligolophus meadii* is a ground dweller in dry, sunny habitats, while *Anelasmocephalus cambridgei*, also a ground dweller, is less restricted in its requirements.

All the other species should still be present on the reserve, and should not be affected by current management. *Dicranopalpus ramosus* has not yet been recorded, but it is spreading rapidly throughout Britain and I have frequently noted it in Suffolk and Essex. Almost certainly it is present, but unrecorded. Some of the older records are unlikely to be repeated without using pitfall traps.

Spiders
Of the 104 species that have been recorded, four are Nationally Scarce. *Enoplognatha mordax* is Notable A and is closely related to *E. ovata*, one of the most abundant British spiders, which is found in the ground and field layers, and is extremely common at The Wick. *E. mordax* is far from common and of the few sites where it has been recorded nationally, most are in Essex and Kent in the upper reaches of salt marshes and in strand-line litter. Two other Wick species are restricted to this habitat: *Pardosa purbeckensis* is a wolf spider that hunts its prey on salt marsh vegetation and tidal litter, whilst *Silometopus ambiguus*, a

small member of the Lynyphiidae, or money spiders, is found especially in tidal litter, although in fewer locations nationwide. This salt marsh habitat is likely to be threatened everywhere by rising sea levels.

The three Notable B species were recorded on low trees, bushes and herbage. *Nigma puella* in Essex has a mainly coastal distribution, and as it has been found in gardens, a warm site may be essential. *Zilla diodia* is a member of the Araneidae, and its orb web can be found in low, sheltered bushes and trees, but one of the two records from The Wick was from the salt marsh. *Tetragnatha pinicola*, the third Notable B species, has a preference for both tall herbage and low foliage in sunny, sheltered situations, so The Wick should be suitable for this species.

Some species at The Wick are rare or scarce in Essex, but do not have a high conservation status nationally. *Peponocranium ludicrum* is one. The male of this small money spider has a greatly enlarged head which must be how its name was derived. It has been found at only three other sites in north Essex, and apparently requires warm, well-drained and barely vegetated ground where it spins its sheet web. *Alopecosa barbipes,* a wolf spider, is another Wick species which is rare in Essex. It has been found at The Wick only on the short rabbit-mown grassland of the main Heath, and this site should be maintained in its present condition. Both of the above species must have suffered loss of habitat at The Wick due to scrub encroachment.

Two crab spiders are worthy of mention. *Xysticus erraticus* and *X. kochi* are both dependent on warm and dry conditions, and *X. erraticus*

may be restricted to the short grass sward found on the main Heath. Most recorded species are generalists found in mixed field and ground layers, including leaf litter. Thick layers of damp leaves in old excavations are home to large numbers of mainly small money spiders. One such area was found to be very rich in *Porrhomma pygmaeum,* with large numbers to the square metre. No species of high conservation value have been found in these places, but there may be some.

Species that live in buildings are under-recorded. An exception is the daddy long-legs spider *Pholcus phalangioides*. Although not recorded frequently by arachnologists because it is limited in the main to warm houses and buildings, this spider has rapidly spread north and is widespread. None of the long-legged spiders, which cause consternation running across the floor – the Teganaria genus – have been recorded, although they are almost certainly present in the house and Centre.

The reserve is now very wooded in places, but some of the species closely associated with woodland do not yet appear to have taken advantage. The prime importance of the reserve to spiders is the less vegetated, sandy substrate which soon warms in the sun. Thankfully, the process of allowing The Wick to become a woodland reserve has been halted. The bulldozer may be regarded as the spider's friend!

Ray Ruffell

(Left) Prostrate web spun in short sward of heathland grass.

(Right, flash photograph) garden spider in web spun inside our kitchen.

Coleoptera:
Beetles

'Look at this big beetle we've found!' In 1979 – my first spring at The Wick – a succession of visitors brought large, leaking beetles into the Centre for me to identify. It happened again in 1980. They were oil beetles. I didn't know it at the time, but they were about to become extinct in the reserve. The adult oil beetle is flightless, and emits a smelly and oily fluid when alarmed. Its larvae are parasitic on solitary bees, which are themselves dependent on bare and disturbed ground in which they tunnel and breed. This spectacular beetle is a good example of an insect that ought to do well at The Wick. We lost that last struggling colony almost certainly because scrub encroached on the bare ground that supported the solitary bees the beetle larvae needed. In recent years our management of the reserve has elevated the regular renewal of bare and disturbed ground to a top priority, to benefit the insects and plants that need these rather uncommon habitats.

Nigel Cuming has spent years surveying the beetles of the reserve. Dead trees, dry grassland, leaf litter, ponds, scrub, sunny paths and shaded thickets – beetles seem to be everywhere, and where there are beetles there also will be Nigel. He has studied them all over the reserve, and I am indebted to him for his commitment and wide-ranging interest in every aspect of the wildlife of the reserve, and for the following notes on a selected group of

beetles, two of which have no English names.

Green tiger beetle
Cicindela campestris. Beautiful gold-green on its upper side, and with yellow marks on the wing cases – the elytra. This predator is built for speed. 12–16 mm in length, it has long legs, large eyes and very well developed, curved and sharply pointed jaws. The underside is a coppery red. The green tiger beetle was first recorded at The Wick by Dan Ambrose in 2002. I found fifteen adults on a visit in May 2004. Typically found on heathlands such as the 'Sandlings' area in Suffolk, it is found in just a few sites in Essex, where the main colony flourishes in the cliffs at Walton on the Naze. Visitors to The Wick should watch out for this exciting beetle in the heathy areas.

Black, Carabid ground beetle
Microlestes minutulus. This tiny species is only 2.7–3.7 mm in length. It was discovered as a species new to Britain in 1995, by B. Eversham and M. Collier who were surveying the Tollesbury area of managed retreat. I found it at The Wick in 1997 in front of the warden's house and have since found it at five other sites in north-east Essex. It seems to require a dry, stony habitat with short vegetation. Unlike *M. maurus,* its smaller congener, it possesses functional hind wings.

Great silver water beetle
Hydrophilus piceus. At 34–38 mm, this completely black aquatic beetle is one of Britain's largest. Found by

Martin Rapley in Kit's pond during a pond-dipping event in 2003, a male and a female were then found there the following year by Sue Foster. The beetles enjoyed a spell in the Centre aquarium, and were then returned to the pond. As far as I know, this constitutes only the third record of the species in north-east Essex. It has been accorded the status of Red Data Book category three, which means it is at risk, having been recorded nationally from fifteen or fewer 10 km squares since 1970.

A 'darkling' beetle
Helops caeruleus. Ken Crawshaw originally recorded this beetle in 1965, in decaying timber in the old barn that once stood on the site of the present Wildlife Garden. Interestingly, Dan Ambrose found it in the same site in March 2002, although the barn is long gone. A deep, metallic violaceous colour, the 14–19 mm beetle requires rotting wood, whether fallen or standing. It is regarded as of nationally Notable 'B' status, which means it is thought to occur in between 31 and 100 10 km squares. It has been found at East Mersea and Thorpe-le-Soken.

Oil beetle
Meloe proscarabaeus. Ken Crawshaw was also the first to record the oil beetle at The Wick, in 1960. Laurie Forsyth saw it in the early 1980s, but it has not been recorded since then. The oil beetle is a large, sluggish blue-black species that wanders in the spring in longish grass. Its size varies greatly between 10 mm and 35 mm, with the female being larger than the male. When threatened, it emits an evil-smelling oil from its joints. The adults are flightless, with abbreviated forewings exposing the bloated abdomen. The life cycle of the oil beetle is remarkable. It is dependant on solitary bees of two genera. Large numbers of eggs are laid in cracks in the soil; the first larval 'instar' – or development stage – has long legs and is very active. Climbing a grass stem, it awaits the arrival of the right sort of bee; it then clings to the bee's leg and is carried to its nest. Below ground, it changes to a more usual grub shape, and devours the eggs and larvae of the bee. Eventually, the adult beetle emerges through the soil. Being flightless, the oil beetle can only colonise new areas in its earliest larval stage, and then only if the right bee comes along. The nearest colony to The Wick is at West Mersea. I greatly hope that one day this splendid insect will once more be found in the reserve.

Minotaur beetle
Typhaeus typhoeus. Named from the mythological creature of ancient Greece, the males of this species have a distinctive trident of forward projecting horns arising from the front margin of the thorax. The 'horns' are used when fighting other males in defence of the brood burrows that are excavated a metre deep in sandy soil. The main shaft gives rise to several side galleries that are provisioned with dung pellets upon which the female lays the eggs. Broad and

Birch and sallow logs piled up year by year form a multi-layered habitat that will benefit many beetle species.

black, the minotaur beetle is between 12 mm and 20 mm in length, and is a member of the *Scarabaeoidea* – the scarabs – which were venerated by the ancient Egyptians. Brood shafts were found by the warden in 2002, and I found ten in 2004. The minotaur is known from only a handful of sites in north-east Essex.

I selected these six beetle species to demonstrate the rich mosaic of habitats at The Wick, and, importantly, their need for careful management. Factors that benefit beetles include dead and decaying timber. Standing dead trees, fallen trunks and branches, or log piles that provide a tower block of varying stages of decay and breakdown are vital, and so are areas with bare ground, or sparse vegetation, and also the non-intervention areas where no management is executed at all. And then there are the aquatic habitats, some of which are sunlit, and some shaded. Fingringhoe Wick can boast a significant and important beetle population that we, as observant naturalists can learn much from, and add to.

Nigel St. John Cuming

Logs with loose, flaking bark are an important beetle habitat.

Walking with nightingales: they are easy to hear – but hard to spot!
Photo: Laurie Forsyth

21st century cockles and Roman oyster shells lie side by side on the beach.
Photo: Laurie Forsyth

Lit by the winter sun, reeds glow along the shoreline of the lake.
Photo: Laurie Forsyth

Nightingales have nested at The Wick for over 40 years.
Photo: David Harrison

The lake in the 1960's with volunteers toiling to level off the island.
Photo: Trust archives

Forty years of natural succession: this view is from the same point as the above photo.
Photo: Laurie Forsyth

The oil beetle is probably extinct at The Wick, but so long as mining bee colonies flourish, there is hope for its return. *Photo: Ian Rose*

Roesel's bush cricket has spread throughout most of the nature reserve. *Photo: Ian Rose*

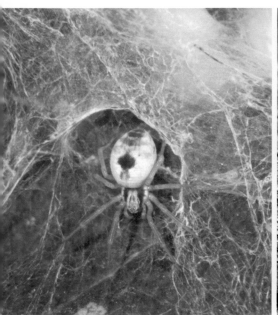

Nigma puella: one of over 100 spider species at The Wick. *Photo: Peter Harvey*

The cream-spot tiger moth is one of the most attractive of more than 700 moths recorded at The Wick since 1961. *Photo: Chris Gibson*

The hairy dragonfly is the most recent large dragonfly to colonise the reserve.
Photo: Ted Benton

Scarlet waxcaps brighten misty autumnal days.
Photo: Ian Rose

Birdsfoot trefoil responds well to mechanised scraping: it is the food plant of the common blue butterfly.
Photo: Laurie Forsyth

Common spotted orchids are superb in some years, but are in slow decline.
Photo: Chris Gibson

The green hairstreak butterfly relies
on gorse and broom.
Photo: Ian Rose

Yellowhammers were once common,
but are now almost gone.
Photo: Bob Glover

Adders flourish at The Wick, and in spring spend most of the day basking.
Photo: Tom Turnbull

Management to create reedbeds on adjacent Army land has brought breeding marsh harriers back to the Colne estuary.
Photo: Bob Glover

The green tiger beetle needs bare, open terrain, and is a recent new arrival.
Photo: Chris Gibson

Wildlife copes well with short spells of snowfall: scenes like this (2005) may be rare in the future if winter temperatures climb.
Photo: Laurie Forsyth

Galls

Years ago, when thrusting through head-high reeds in the Scrape I came across a few reed stems that were swollen at the top, and rock hard. Jerry Bowdrey identified them as cigar galls. At 8 cm they must be among the largest of British galls. Caused by a grey-brown fly, the gall develops and provides shelter and food for the fly larva inside. Jerry is Curator of Colchester Natural History Museum, and an acknowledged authority on galls and the insects that cause them. I am grateful to him for introducing me to the strange world of galls, and for the following account of the galls and the organisms that induce them at The Wick. He has also contributed the report on plant bugs (Heteroptera) that follows this report.

A gall is an abnormal growth produced by a plant or other host under the influence of another organism. It involves enlargement and/or proliferation of host cells and provides both shelter and food or nutrients for the invading organism. Gall-inducing organisms are enormously diverse, ranging from single-celled plants and animals, through micro fungi, to multicellular animals and plants. In turn, they affect a wide range of hosts from the algae to higher plants. The vast majority of galls are found on leaves, but every part of a plant can be galled.

The serious study of galls in Essex dates back to the 19th century, although there is no record of studies in the area now occupied by the nature reserve.

Recording at The Wick began in 1981 as part of a county gall survey that I initiated: it culminated in a survey by the British Plant Gall Society in 2003.

The casual observer will notice large and obvious galls such as the oak apple and oak marble which are created by a tiny wasp in the buds of mature oaks and also saplings. The red, showy robin's pincushion gall is closely related and found on wild rose. The cola nut gall and the knopper gall are also found on oak: they are both relatively new species which arrived in the late 20th century.

In damper areas, sallow thickets support a large range of species including those induced by gall midges of the genus *Rabdophaga*, whose galls on twigs are particularly noticeable in winter. John Skinner and I recorded galls of *Rabdophaga salicis* at The Wick in 1981 – the first Essex record for many years. Another significant species is *Asphondylia pilosa*, a midge that induces galls on buds of broom. It was found at The Wick by Michael Chinery during the 2003 survey and is a new record for Essex.

The picture-winged flies (Tephritidae) include several species that induce galls. Perhaps the largest is caused by *Urophora cardui*, which induces an egg-shaped gall in the stems of creeping thistle, usually in plants growing in damp areas. The adult fly has a 'W'-shaped black mark on each wing and can sometimes be seen signalling with these to its mate, from a thistle flower.

Red swellings in willowherb stems are often conspicuous. They are induced by the micro-moth *Mompha nodicollela*, a Notable B species nationally. It is thought to have been spread around the country via railway wagons! Galls induced by mites are generally smaller but often occur in large numbers. Their red colour makes them conspicuous on the green leaves of their host. *Aceria varius* is an uncommon species that induces tufts of hairs or erinea on the underside of aspen leaves. Its discovery at The Wick in 1982 added another new species to the county list.

Gall ecology and Fingringhoe Wick

Gall inducers are dependent on their host plants. It is likely therefore that the fauna in a comparatively active habitat such as a working gravel pit in the 1940s and 1950s would have been initially quite impoverished. When extraction ceased in 1959, a pioneer flora evolved into scrub and secondary woodland. At some point in this natural succession, host plant diversity was at its maximum, when we would have expected the maximum number of gall-inducing species to have occurred. Management of the nature reserve is now geared to slowing the process of natural succession, and even reversing it in some areas. Inevitably, as plant species died out their galls were lost, and were replaced by new host plant species and new galls.

Gall inducers are often very mobile

and it would not be long before newly established plant species acquired their complement of galls, especially as invertebrates are often attracted to plants growing under some degree of physiological stress such as water shortage, which is likely on the light and gravelly soils of The Wick.

Management of the reserve has created a mosaic of habitats supporting a diverse flora, which is providing a wide range of hosts for gall-inducing organisms. It is likely that with further surveys and increasing knowledge many new species will be added to the list.

Jerry Bowdrey

Cigar gall on reed in Kit's pond. Long after the first inhabitants have gone it will be used by other species.

Heteroptera:

Plant bugs

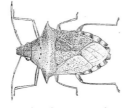

The earliest Heteroptera records at The Wick go back to the 1960s: Tony Richardson and other members of Colchester Natural History Society dipped some of the ponds and found numerous aquatic species. Other species have been added since then as a result of general fieldwork and also nocturnal moth trapping sessions by CNHS. As might be expected in an old gravel pit, the most interesting and uncommon of the terrestrial bug species are those associated with dry and sparsely vegetated ground. Such species might have been early colonists of suitable micro-habitats both during and after gravel extraction. They could be expected to have declined as vegetation encroached on their preferred habitat.

Fortunately, current reserve management aimed at increasing open habitat has ensured the continued survival of such species. For example, *Syromastus rhombeus* is a local species inhabiting dry, sparsely vegetated ground, found so far in only one other locality in the Colchester area. It has a distinctive diamond shape and is sometimes confused with the common squash bug *Coreus marginatus*, which occurs in large numbers on docks and related plants. Another species occupying dry

habitats is the local *Alydus calcaratus*, a dark, well-camouflaged and fast moving bug of open ground which flashes a bright abdomen when in flight. If this defensive ruse fails, it can emit an unpleasant odour reminiscent of dog dung! *Alydus* is known from several similar dry sites around Colchester. The local *Ceraleptus lividus* is another dry ground specialist and is associated with clovers.

Perhaps the most interesting species found so far is the slow-moving *Spathocera dahlmanni*. This is a Nationally Scarce (Notable A) bug associated with sheep's sorrel growing on dry, sandy ground. It was discovered by Nigel Cuming in 2004. The only other recent county records are from Middlewick MoD ranges in Colchester. At The Wick, this bug has undoubtedly benefited from the re-creation of the bare ground habitat.

Picromerus bidens is a predatory shield bug that feeds on insect larvae and other small prey. Found in a variety of habitats with tall vegetation and/or low branches where such prey occurs, it is easily distinguished from similar sized bugs as the pronotum bears two large lateral spines. Although classified as common nationally, it is somewhat local in north-east Essex. Far commoner is the gorse shield bug *Piezodorus lituratus*, a large, green bug that turns reddish brown in winter. In spring it can be found sunning itself on gorse stems, but it moves to other plant species that are more leafy after the gorse seed is shed. Broom is an alternative host. Gorse and the shield bug are always likely to be present on the light soils of The Wick.

A second group of species that is well represented on the reserve includes those associated with aquatic habitats. Water bugs are active fliers and can colonise new pools almost as fast as they are formed. It is thought they can detect water by the reflection from its surface. They include water stick-insect *Ranatra linearis*, water scorpion *Nepa cinerea*, saucer bug *Ilocoris cimicoides* and water measurer *Hydrometra stagnorum*. The process of natural succession in ponds eventually leads to dry ground. This could have severe effects on populations of aquatic Heteroptera, but reserve management aimed at keeping ponds in good condition has maintained populations of the open water species. The invasive, alien swamp stonecrop however may be detrimental to these species where small ponds become choked with vegetation. Future fieldwork will doubtless add many species to the reserve list, especially in the newly created open areas.

Jerry Bowdrey

The Old Farm pond is the oldest pond on the reserve, and may well be the richest in aquatic invertebrates.

Hymenoptera:
Bees, wasps and ants

Before 1994, the hornet was almost unknown at The Wick. Since then this magnificent wasp has become a daily summer sighting. In 1995 a queen built a nest inside the Thurstable hide, and soon workers were droning through the hide's viewing slots and the birders were in full retreat. Hornets 6 – Twitchers 0. The hide remained closed for months. The hymenoptera – the bees, wasps and ants – flourish in gravel pits. Adrian Knowles has studied them at The Wick for years, and it is due to his work that their habitat needs are firmly entrenched in the management plan. I am grateful to him for the following report.

There are nearly 600 species of bees, wasps and ants in Britain, and over 300 species have been recorded in Essex. You know the bumblebees, honeybees and the yellow and black social wasps that gatecrash your picnic, but they are only a tiny proportion of the total. The vast majority of bees and wasps are small, unobtrusive, and live an essentially solitary life unnoticed by the public. So far, over 130 species have been recorded from The Wick – an impressive total for a single site. Within this total, nineteen species are listed as being Nationally Scarce, and three are nationally threatened Red Data Book species.

Bees, wasps and ants are among the few animal groups that were attracted to The Wick when it was a working pit. Many are called 'mining' bees or 'digger' wasps because they construct underground nests. Bare, sandy cliffs, spoil heaps and even hard, compacted ground formed when the quarry was being worked would have suited many species, although their residency would have been only temporary! Since then, the nature reserve has evolved and matured. As their habitats decreased in area due to the onset of scrub and woodland, some of the species needing bare, sunny ground have been replaced by the many species that nest in holes in dead wood, hollow plant stems and branches.

Many species are as industrious as the honeybee. Some bees and wasps however have become 'cuckoo' species. Others have become parasites that lay their eggs within the nests of others: the larva of the parasite hatches first and devours the larva of the host, and its food store. Probably the most

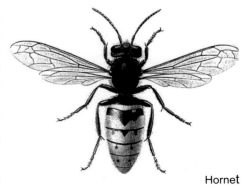

Hornet

The burrows of mining bees and wasps on the vertical face of The Mound.

spectacular of these are the ruby-tailed wasps – small, fast-moving insects that sparkle with iridescent red, blue and green. *Chrysura radians* is a species new to Essex, and it was discovered at The Wick in 2000 on a large dead log outside the Centre, where it was scouting for nests of leaf-cutter bees to raid.

The often complex ecology of insects requires complex conservation considerations. A good example is another ruby-tailed wasp, *Hedychrum niemelai*. The wasp is so scarce and threatened that it is listed in the British Red Data Book for insects (category RDB 3: Rare). One reason for its rarity may be that it is a parasite of another Red Data Book species – the digger wasp *Cerceris quinquefasciata* (RDB 3). This wasp is so threatened that it is the subject of a national Biodiversity Action Plan, and it is also included in English Nature's Species Recovery programme. There are decades-old records for this digger wasp at The Wick, and in 2002 its parasite *Hedychrum* (mentioned above) was found near Kit's pond, suggesting that the digger wasp itself was still present. I found it in August 2004 whilst inspecting one of the nearly bare banks on the East Heath.

It is a little surprising that only one other Red Data Book species has been recorded at The Wick. This is the bee-wolf *Philanthus triangulum* (RDB 2), a digger wasp that earns its name by catching honeybees and paralysing them, before flying off with its prey and then taking them underground as food for its larvae. It is quite a sight to see this large yellow and black wasp cruising along with a honeybee slung beneath its body. Another group of wasps has the perilous tendency to catch spiders as prey items for their larvae. The striking spider-hunting wasp *Episyron rufipes* can be seen in large numbers on sandy ground in the picnic area: the males are looking for suitable mates, and the females are hunting for spiders to take to their underground nests.

Some species recorded at The Wick are tied to the coastal habitat as much as to the old gravel pit, such as the mining bee *Colletes halophilus*. Its name is loosely translated as 'salt-loving'. The coastal association lies with its preferred source of pollen: sea aster flowers. In late summer this striking bee – it has gingery hairs on its thorax, and white hair stripes on its black abdominal segments – can also be seen gathering nectar from bramble flowers. Other bees have equally restricted pollen requirements for their larvae. The large, ginger and black mining bee *Andrena clarkella* is one of the earliest to be seen in the reserve each year: it

gathers pollen from the early willow catkins. *Andrena labiata* is smaller, and has an association with speedwell flowers and occasionally with greater stitchwort.

Changes with the passing of time have meant the loss of some species, and the arrival of others. Sometimes, species are lost no matter what steps are taken to protect them. There are old records at The Wick for the bumblebees *Bombus humilis* and *Bombus sylvarum*. Both are national Biodiversity Action Plan species, and both are now rooted in Thameside, Essex, following decades of decline in lowland Britain. They are unlikely to return to Fingringhoe Wick. For many species in the nature reserve however, large-scale mechanised management in recent years has turned back the clock of natural succession. Bare ground, thinly vegetated banks and flower-rich grassland provide the disturbed habitat that many bees and wasps call home. It may be no coincidence that the rare digger wasp *Cerceris quinquefasciata* was found on the East Heath in 2004 just months after the soil was mechanically scraped to provide the exact conditions it, and other bees, wasps and ants need.

Adrian Knowles

Lepidoptera
Moths and butterflies

There is a birch-fringed glade close to the Trout Pool. It is the place where in 1966 Geoff Pyman saw the last dingy skipper butterfly recorded at The Wick. 'I think it would be good to keep it open and sunny, just in case there is still a caterpillar or two.' His optimistic advice was given in 1980, and to keep the faith the clearing has been kept like that. Geoff recorded the moths and butterflies of the reserve in the early days. Brian Goodey however was the first to conduct a mercury-vapour-lamp moth survey spanning the seasons, and to produce a complete systematic list of the moths in 1987. The wealth of moths reflects the richness of the flora and the variety of habitats within the reserve. I think the average visitor would be astounded to learn that over 700 moth species are present at The Wick. Brian, who is the County Recorder for Lepidoptera has kindly contributed the following report.

Moths

With the right conditions, it is possible in a single night to attract nearly 200 species of moth to a mercury-vapour lamp at the reserve. By day, a further 100 types of smaller moth, known as leaf-miners, may be recorded during the autumn months. In total, 28 butterflies and 716 moths have been seen at The Wick, indicating that it is one of the most species-rich sites in Essex. Not that it has been particularly over-worked: recording of moths at the reserve has been rather sporadic over the years, with most of the effort taking place during the mid-1980s to the early 1990s and very little afterwards, so doubtless more species await discovery.

From the air the reserve looks like an island bordered by the River Colne to the east, extensive salt marsh to the south, and arable fields to the north and west. It lies just 1.3 km from the Roman River Valley with its entomologically-rich habitats. This, coupled with the adjacent salt marshes allows a variety of insects to reach the reserve either as visitors or as breeding stock. In many ways the reserve resembles Essex in miniature, with areas of salt marsh, scrub, gorse heathland and reedbeds, each with its own characteristic fauna.

Maintaining this diversity of habitats should be high on the list of future management plans for the reserve. In particular, scrub must not encroach on flower-rich grassland, which is so valuable for nectaring insects as well as for supporting such moths as the six-belted clearwing *Bembecia ichneumoniformis*, which needs birdsfoot trefoil to thrive. *Coleophora fuscicornis*, which requires smooth tare for its larvae, was discovered as a British species in 1973 and Fingringhoe Wick is one of only seven known breeding sites in the country. Areas containing mosses, such a feature of some of the open parts of the reserve, are also critical for moths such as *Synaphe punctalis* and *Chionodes fumatella* and are vulnerable to the advance of scrub such as gorse, although gorse is valuable for providing shelter for roosting insects and as a foodplant for larvae.

Scrubby areas also support the rose plume *Cnaemidophorus rhododactyla*, a scarce moth in Britain which, as its name suggests, needs dog rose to thrive. Other local species that prefer scrub and secondary woodland have been found at the reserve; these include birch mocha *Cyclophora albipunctata*, sloe pug *Pasiphila chloerata*, sloe carpet *Aleucis distinctata*, broom-tip *Chesias rufata*, and blossom underwing *Orthosia miniosa*.

Woodland, especially on the northern and western parts of the reserve, supports *Stigmella samiatella* and *Coleophora laricella* on the larches bordering the entry road; clouded magpie *Abraxas sylvata* and dusky-lemon sallow *Xanthia gilvago* on elm; and in the sunnier parts *Micropterix aruncella* and the long-horn *Nemophora degeerella*. Two woodland moths, white-spotted pinion *Cosmia diffinis* and beautiful hook-tip *Laspeyria flexula,* have much declined and may have disappeared from the reserve, though the former may one day return.

As may be expected, moths favouring saltings, reedbeds and fresh-water marshes are well represented and these include local species such as *Coleophora deviella*, *Calamotropha paludella*, striped wainscot *Mythimna pudorina*, southern wainscot *M. straminea*, Mathew's wainscot *M. favicolor*, star-wort *Cucullia asteris*, reed dagger *Simyra albovenosa*, crescent striped *Apamea oblonga*, twin-spotted wainscot *Archanara geminipuncta*, silky wainscot *Chilodes maritimus*, and dotted fan-foot *Macrochilo cribrumalis*. The bag-worm moth *Epichnopterix retiella* was recorded during the 1980s but it seems to have disappeared, as it has from other saltings in Essex.

Other coastal-orientated moths include mullein wave *Scopula marginepunctata*, rosy wave *S. emutaria*, yellow belle *Semiaspilates ochrearia*, water ermine *Spilosoma urticae*, Archer's dart *Agrotis vestigialis* and the coastal form of northern drab *Orthosia opima.*

Although many people have visited The Wick recording Lepidoptera, two people stand out. Geoff Pyman worked at the reserve and was also County Recorder for the larger moths and butterflies for many years. Geoff was able to do limited recording himself, but also helped in the identification of specimens brought to him. Maitland Emmet was a specialist microlepidopterist who favoured the leaf-miners in particular and visited the reserve on a number of occasions, adding to its impressive list species that otherwise would have been omitted.

The future of the Lepidoptera at Fingringhoe Wick seems assured under current management practices. Many of the habitats it boasts are transient in nature, and species that occupy them need to be highly mobile in nature, lessening the risks of local extinctions caused by disease, predation or rising tides due to global warming.

Brian Goodey

Butterflies

By 1966, the dingy skipper and ringlet were both gone from the reserve. The grayling persisted until 1971, until it too became extinct at The Wick. Among the Pieridae, the three common whites are regularly recorded each year. It is likely that 40 years ago the gravel workings supported very many cruciferous arable weed species, to the benefit of the orange-tip. Today however its numbers are very low, and centred on the old grazing meadow where lady's smock still grows. The brimstone occasionally visits the reserve in spring, as does the clouded yellow in summer. Among the Lycaenidae, the holly blue is recorded in small numbers each year: famously cyclical, it can fluctuate as it did in 1990 when it was in good numbers. The common blue is more stable, and with current management methods much to the liking of birdsfoot trefoil, its larval food plant, it seems safe. Summer brings the usual sightings of the purple hairstreak near our large oaks. In contrast, the white-letter hairstreak is a dark horse. Sightings in 1996 and 2002 of single specimens on bramble flowers suggest that somewhere, a small colony is hanging on. It rarely moves far from the elms where the eggs are laid, and is unlikely to have flown into the reserve from outside. Gorse and broom are the larval foodplants of the lovely green hairstreak. Both plants respond well to scrub clearance, and in some years the butterfly is widespread. I attract it into the garden by planting green alkanet. My birthday in May 1997 was enhanced by the sight of at least 40 feeding on the blue flowers. Abundant colonies of sheep's sorrel on the main Heath support the small copper. In summer, they feed on the flowers of the bell heather that was introduced to the acid heath many years ago. Brian Watts recorded the brown argus in 1996, but the attempted colonisation apparently failed.

Visitors are most aware of the large and colourful species in the Nymphalidae. None are as common as they once were: the peacock is perhaps the most common, with the migrant painted lady and red admiral close behind. The comma is present in small numbers, and appears to be stable. After a spectacular decline in its population in the 1990s, there are signs of recovery by the small tortoiseshell. An overwintered Camberwell beauty was seen by Martin Rapley in April 1996, and Geoff Pyman recorded a worn silver-washed fritillary in 1977.

In 1980 the developing woodland habitat at The Wick attracted a new member of the Satyridae. Brian Watts recorded the first speckled wood, and the species is now quite common in suitable sites throughout the reserve. In some years, the grass-feeding meadow brown and gatekeeper are both numerous. For several years before 2003, I feared we had lost the small heath, but a small colony was found then on the East Heath by Jonathan Forsyth. Current management methods are likely to result in more of the open, short grassland it favours. Sadly, there is no management recipe that will help the wall brown: a year when one is seen is a good year.

In several ways, rabbits are a boon to the reserve because they help to keep scrub in check, and create localised disturbance by digging and scuffling. Unfortunately they also closely graze flowers and grasses, which might otherwise be a source of nectar for butterflies, or food for their caterpillars. Our three members of the Hesperidae all need long grass: the small, large and Essex skipper are all found mainly in the old grazing meadow, and despite my concerns about the effects of rabbits they seem to be holding their own.

Laurie Forsyth

Common blue butterflies on knapweed; their caterpillars need birdsfoot trefoil as their foodplant. *Courtesy English Nature.*

Odonata
Dragonflies and damselflies

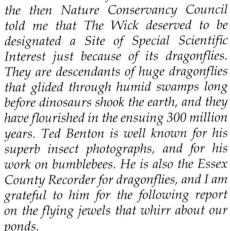

Long ago, the late Colin Ranson of the then Nature Conservancy Council told me that The Wick deserved to be designated a Site of Special Scientific Interest just because of its dragonflies. They are descendants of huge dragonflies that glided through humid swamps long before dinosaurs shook the earth, and they have flourished in the ensuing 300 million years. Ted Benton is well known for his superb insect photographs, and for his work on bumblebees. He is also the Essex County Recorder for dragonflies, and I am grateful to him for the following report on the flying jewels that whirr about our ponds.

Dragonflies are fierce predators, both as adults and during the early, aquatic stages of their life-history. The bodies of still or moving water that provide their breeding habitat need to be rich in the smaller invertebrates on which the dragonfly larvae feed. These smaller invertebrates, in turn, need well-vegetated ponds or rivers to provide them with food and cover. In addition, the adult dragonflies require insect-rich dry-land habitat within flying distance of their breeding habitats. Here they shelter during the vulnerable early stage after emerging from the water, and hunt for their prey. The management of the water-margins is of particular importance:

this is the transitional zone, where adult dragonflies emerge from their larval 'skin', stretch their wings and begin life as flying insects. It is also the site for territorial activity, mating and egg-laying.

Fingringhoe Wick provides all these habitat features in abundance. The aquatic habitat takes the form of a complex of old ponds retained since its days as a working sand and gravel pit as well as several newly created ones. The terrestrial habitat at The Wick, too, is just what the dragonflies need; a mosaic of open heath and grassland, scrub and woodland. The tracks through the reserve are flowery and insect rich, and are an additional hunting ground for the adult dragonflies.

Over the years, the reserve has provided habitat for a remarkably stable number of breeding dragonfly species, though with some interesting changes. A survey in the 1980s reported fifteen species, and the figure today is seventeen.

Several species that are rapid colonisers of newly created or cleared ponds, with little or no marginal vegetation, are the common blue damselfly *Enallagma cyathigerum* and the black-tailed skimmer *Orthetrum cancellatum*. Both breed at The Wick, and the latter species is especially in evidence along the open banks of the lake. Other common species, such as the blue-tailed damselfly *Ischnura elegans*, the azure damselfly *Coenagrion puella* and the common darter dragonfly *Sympetrum striolatum* are to be found almost anywhere on the reserve.

The large red damselfly *Pyrrhosoma nymphula* is usually the first dragonfly to be seen on the wing in early spring. It is soon followed, about the middle of May, by The Wick's two localised 'chaser' dragonflies: the four-spotted *Libellula quadrimaculata*, and the broad-bodied *L. depressa*. These tend to stay close to their breeding ponds – notably the old farm pond and the newly created pond close to Kit's pond. The four-spotted chaser is tolerant of brackish water and breeds also in Kit's pond. One of The Wick's 'specialities' also flies from mid-May and can be seen through the month of June. This is the hairy dragonfly *Brachytron pratense*, the earliest of the hawker dragonflies. Until the mid-1990s it was considered a scarce species in Britain, and had only one known site in Essex. Since then it has colonised several new areas, and has been breeding in the old farm pond at The Wick in recent years. July is the best time to see some of the other, spectacular hawker dragonflies that breed in several of the reserve's ponds: the southern, migrant and brown hawkers *Aeshna cyanea*, *A. mixta* and *A. grandis*, together with the magnificent emperor *Anax imperator*. The latter species is on the wing earlier than July, however, and continues to fly well into August. The migrant hawker (which seems to like to hunt in groups, unlike its more solitary relatives) continues to fly until November in some years. The southern and migrant hawkers lay their eggs in damp mud or moss at the edge of ponds, rather than in the water – Pine pond is a good place to see this.

The more densely vegetated ponds are the best places to look for two of the more elusive of The Wick's damselflies: the common and scarce emeralds *Lestes sponsa* and *L. dryas*. Neither species is common, but the scarce emerald was thought to be extinct in Britain by 1980. In fact, this proved not to be the case, and Essex is now one of the national strongholds for this species. It colonises ditches and shallow ponds in the last stages of their drying out, and can cope with habitats that dry out during the summer months. It colonised The Wick in the 1980s, and is now back again, breeding in the Scrape, and possibly elsewhere on the reserve: the old farm pond would be a good place to look. The common emerald can be seen 'skulking', wings partly open, among reed stems in several of the ponds. Both species lay their eggs, while still paired, in the stems of reeds or rushes above the water line. Another species of the more abundantly vegetated ponds is the ruddy darter *Sympetrum sanguineum*, formerly a very localised species that has become more common in recent years. Unlike its later-flying relative, the common darter, it is not often seen later than the end of August.

Finally, there is a very exciting new

arrival: the small red-eyed damselfly *Erythromma viridulum*. This was first noticed in Britain in July 1999 at a pond in north-east Essex. It is now well established in ponds throughout Essex, and has spread to other eastern and southern counties of Britain. Soon after its discovery it was reported by several observers at The Wick on Kit's pond, and in 2004 was seen on the newly created pond close to Kit's pond, as well as on the lake. At the latter site several males were seen basking on floating leaves, and pairs were also watched as the females laid eggs.

The continuing diversity of dragonfly species at The Wick is testimony to the active management work that has been carried out over the years. Further mechanised scrub clearance and the creation of new ponds to maintain the diversity of aquatic and marginal habitats can only maintain and even enhance the value of the reserve for dragonflies in the future.

Ted Benton

Kit's pond is one of the best breeding sites for dragonflies at The Wick. The small red-eyed damselfly colonised the brackish pond in 2001. Brown hawker, emperor, broad-bodied chaser, hairy dragonfly and ruddy darter are among the fourteen species breeding here.

Orthoptera:
Crickets and grasshoppers

Nature reserve wardens know they are ageing not when the policemen look younger, but when they can no longer hear the love songs  *– or stridulations – of grasshoppers and bush crickets. For years I have relied on others telling me what was plainly audible to them in the grasses just a few feet away. Alan Wake was the Essex County Recorder for the Orthoptera – the bush crickets, true crickets, groundhoppers and grasshoppers. I am very grateful to him for the following report on a important group of insects of which, to my embarrassment, I know too little.*

The native orthoptera of Great Britain, excluding the offshore islands, is very small in comparison with most insect orders and numbers just 27 species. Of these, eight are extremely rare and occur in just a handful of sites, whilst others are highly specialised in their habitat requirements. As far as Essex is concerned, eighteen of these species have been recorded at some time. Three are highly dubious, and one of these – the field cricket – was found only once, near to Southend on Sea. It was thought possible that it had been introduced from abroad on military equipment, and has not been refound.

So how does Fingringhoe Wick fare? Currently there are records for nine native species, plus one established alien, the house cricket, *Acheta domesticus,* which was found in 1989. I am reasonably certain that two other species will be found, whilst a further two could inhabit the reserve in the future. The following is a summary of the The Wick's native orthoptera.

Oak bush cricket
Meconema thalassinum. As its name suggests, it inhabits oak but can be found on a wide range of shrubs and bushes. Common and under no threat.

Dark bush cricket
Pholidoptera griseoaptera. Very common everywhere, particularly in bramble. It is more likely to be seen late in the day. Not threatened.

Roesel's bush cricket
Metrioptera roeselii. Essex was once the stronghold of this insect, but it has since considerably extended its range. Common, especially in the estuarine areas and is under no threat.

Short-winged conehead
Conocephalus dorsalis. Mainly found on coastal grasses, rushes and reeds, and is therefore restricted mainly to these areas. It may inhabit reeds on some of the ponds. Not threatened.

Speckled bush cricket
Leptophyes punctatissima. Common in nettles and shrubby areas. This insect is difficult to locate due to its faint stridulation. It is under no threat.

Slender ground hopper
Tetrix subulata. Found in just a few areas. It prefers damp areas, and due to its small size and lack of stridulation it is difficult to locate. Probably it is under recorded. Providing the damp areas are retained it should not be threatened.

Common field grasshopper
Chorthippus brunneus. A very common insect found mainly in areas of dry, sparse grass. Under no threat.

Meadow grasshopper
Chorthippus parallelus. Also common in grassland but prefers lusher, slightly damper areas. Not threatened.

Lesser marsh grasshopper
Chorthippus albomarginatus. Until recently it preferred maritime grassland, but it now shows a nation-wide tendency to move into less estuarine areas. Under no threat.

What of the future? I am quite sure two species inhabit The Wick and are waiting to be found. Long-winged conehead, *Conocephalus discolor* has undergone an amazing expansion of its range in the past decade. Previously restricted to the New Forest area in Hampshire, it has spread across the country. It has colonised and is breeding in Hertfordshire, and has been recorded in several areas of Essex. Very catholic in its habitat, it could appear anywhere in scrubby grassland or shrub areas. The other, the common ground hopper *Tetrix undulata*, is a very small insect. It is often found with the slender ground hopper but generally prefers drier conditions. It has almost certainly been overlooked at The Wick, due to its small size, lack of stridulation and its cryptic colouring.

Two further species could possibly appear on the reserve. Great green bush cricket *Tettigonia viridissima* has been found in the Colchester area, in the Hythe marshes and in the nearby Rowhedge Pits: it also occurs sporadically along the Essex coast. Conditions on the reserve are certainly suitable. It is a large insect, and likes stridulating from the top of vegetation during the afternoon and into the evening. The other, the mottled grasshopper *Myrmeleotettix maculata*, is rare in Essex, and requires rather sparse grassland and lichen heath. It has been found at the rear of shingle areas at Colne Point. Conditions at The Wick could be favourable in some areas, although we do not know how long it might take for this insect to exploit areas which have been worked for gravel.

Given its relatively small size, the nature reserve is now one of the best areas in Essex for orthoptera, and is likely only to improve.

Alan Wake

Flora

We are fortunate that a botanist of the calibre of the late Stan Jermyn was at hand to monitor the developing flora of The Wick and to carry out the first botanical survey of the reserve in 1962/3. He found about 350 species of flowering plants, grasses and ferns in a site that was then sunlit, almost treeless, studded with numerous small ponds and still bare in many areas. I carried out a survey in 1982, and also found about 350 species. The two lists are very different. The following is a summary of the main plant groups in the 1960s, and the same groups in 2004 following over 40 years of natural succession.

The chaotic, tumbled spoil heaps of 1962 were ideal for the cabbage family (Brassicaceae). Many species are weeds of cultivation or disturbed ground, and they were probably the first to colonise The Wick. Fourteen species were found in the first survey, and I found twelve in 1982. Lady's smock still flowers each spring in the old grazing meadow; dittander – a speciality of north-east Essex – and English scurvy grass still grow on the north salt marsh.

The nutrient-poor, well drained and sandy soils of the old pit also suited the large pea-flower family (Fabaceae). In the first survey, 27 species were noted ranging from 2 m-high gorse to the tiny, prostrate common birdsfoot, and including clovers, medicks, vetches, trefoils and tares. We have lost strawberry and subterranean clovers, bush vetch and probably grass vetchling, but 23 species are still present. Our management priority of scraping to achieve bare ground will continually create new habitats for these plants which are so characteristic of gravel pits.

Very little escaped the eye of Stan Jermyn, but somehow he missed the pignut growing in the old grazing meadow. Perhaps the grass was too high. However, he recorded fifteen other species of the carrot family (Apiaceae). Since 1982 we have lost wild angelica, wild celery, wild carrot, wild parsnip and hemlock water dropwort. I suspect the latter was

Wild honeysuckle is rapidly spreading in the young woodland.

planted. Sickle hare's-ear, an alien from southern Europe was introduced to the reserve by Stan at two sites in 1964, but succumbed to scrub in the 1990s. Ten species are still present in 2004.

Colt's-foot, one of the daisy family (Asteraceae), with its leafless flower stems was one of the very first plants to colonise the wet sand and gravel at the edges of the ponds. Over 50 species of this very large family were identified by Stan, of which 36 are still present. Marsh sowthistle, a plant not on his list but which he later planted to prevent its likely extinction in Essex, is flourishing and spreading in reedy areas. Among the lost species are great burdock, welted thistle, sea mayweed, hoary ragwort and – a note of personal regret – the attractive blue fleabane.

The aromatic mint family (Lamiaceae) has held its own over the years, although there have been changes.

Twelve species were noted in 1962. Yellow archangel – now gone – is a surprise: if it was on the north boundary it supports my idea that old woodland once flanked that side of the reserve, whilst wood sage is another pointer in the same direction. Greater calamint has since been re-identified across the county as lesser calamint. It is rapidly spreading in the grass surrounding the Centre.

I have always admired the staying power of sand spurrey. In the barren, arid waste of the picnic area it is driven over by coaches, crushed by feet and eaten by rabbits. Stan Jermyn found it there in 1962 and it is still present. He identified fifteen other species in the pink family (Caryophyllaceae); in 2004 there are sixteen species from that family among the mouse-ears, stitchworts, chickweeds, spurreys, pearlworts, sandworts and campions.

Grasses from the neighbouring field margins and hedgerows were swift

Bell heather and ling were introduced into the acidic soil of the heath.

Sea lavender forms purple swathes on the salt marshes in July.

to colonise the old gravel workings. In 1963 the survey listed 37 grass species in habitats ranging from spoil heaps to the salt marsh, and from ponds to the carpark. In 2004 there are 38 grasses: they vary in size from the 2 m reed to the tiny silvery hair-grass, which was not recorded in 1962. One of our management aims is to increase the number of open areas, some of which will eventually form new grassland.

Below ground level, the old excavations have developed a humid micro-climate that especially suits ferns. I suspect two species – royal fern and black spleenwort – were planted. The latter is a species of rocks and walls, rather than the soil where it was found. Both are gone, as is adder's-tongue fern, which is usually a plant of old grassland. The nine survivors include hart's-tongue, polypody, lady and soft-shield ferns.

Stan Jermyn found bee orchid and common spotted orchid, and they are both still present. The latter has declined from several thousand plants in five colonies in 1979 to a few score plants in 2004. A third orchid species – the southern marsh orchid – was known in the mid-1960s: it was lost, and then a few plants were refound in 1987. It has now gone – again. He also found brookweed, which was very rare in 1962 and is now probably extinct in Essex, and yellow wort, which is usually found on chalk. Both are gone. He missed another very unusual plant in the shape of stag's-horn club moss, which is more often found on acid moorland but which has occasionally turned up at southern gravel pits. It did not survive the drought years of the 1990s, which also caused the almost total demise of *Sphagnum* moss at The Wick. 1976 saw the arrival of an aggressive alien aquatic plant, the fearsome swamp stonecrop. Decades later, it is seemingly unstoppable in the Trout Pool where its smothering sprawl has eliminated spiked water-milfoil.

The flora of the reserve is now very different to the one Stan Jermyn saw. It will continue to change in response to habitat factors, droughts, non-stop rabbit grazing – and now climate change.

Laurie Forsyth

Bryophyta
Mosses and liverworts

Way back in 1979 Ken Adams alerted me to the importance of the nature reserve for bryophytes – the mosses and liverworts. He told me that five different Sphagnum bog mosses were present: in arid Essex that is remarkable. Since then, natural succession and other problems have hit the mosses and liverworts hard. Ken is the County Recorder for these interesting and beautiful plants, and I am grateful to him for the following report.

From the 1960s to the mid-1980s, the gravel workings of Fingringhoe Wick provided a wide range of habitats, and formed one of the richest bryophyte localities in Essex. There were extensive *Sphagnum* bogs in the winter-wet hollows, and a good acidic bryophyte flora on the open, flat areas and gravel cliffs. In several winter-wet hollows the aquatic liverwort *Riccia fluitans* was to be found in abundance, and *Blasia pusilla* occurred just above the water line on the otherwise bare gravel margins of some of the larger pools. Only a tiny scrap of *Riccia* could be found beside the Bunkhouse pond in 2004, the other smaller pools having been totally blanketed by the alien swamp stonecrop *Crassula helmsii*, a flowering aquatic plant from Australia. This plant has obliterated all but one of the *Sphagnum* colonies and has enveloped most of the

marginal areas around the larger pools. By the 1990s much of the lichen on the main Heath had been invaded by the southern hemisphere alien moss *Campylopus introflexus*, which spreads as bright green lawns along the gravel paths. It fruits readily, and is also spread by shoot-tip fragments. It has been matched in abundance in recent years by another alien: the leafy-liverwort *Lophocolea semiteres*, again from the southern hemisphere. It now blankets many of the damp, sandy and gravelly banks around the margins of the hollows and the edges of paths. In fact, this alien has been present at The Wick since at least 1973: a specimen I collected then and tentatively identified as *Chiloscyphus polyanthos* was noted as being atypical in form and rather pale in colour. On re-examination it has turned out to be this species.

The north-facing, old sand martin cliff once supported a colony of *Pogonatum aloides*. The cliff has since eroded, but there are plans for its future restoration. The rarest bryophyte ever recorded on the reserve is *Bryum knowltonii*: a Red Data book species found by Eric Saunders in July 1963. It is now known from only a handful of sites around our coasts, and occurs in damp dune slacks close to the sea. Unfortunately, Eric did not give exact details of where he found it, and most of the likely area is now enveloped in scrub.

Atmospheric pollution at The Wick would appear to be still quite high, as despite the presence of numerous suitable neutral-barked elder trees on the reserve, very few of the epiphytic mosses and liverworts that are sensitive to sulphur dioxide (SO_2) had returned by the autumn of 2004, in contrast to their spectacular recovery over most of the rest of Essex and the London area. Although *Orthotrichum affine* was found luxuriant and fruiting, only small fragments of *Zygodon viridissimus* and *Orthotrichum lyellii* were in evidence, and only one patch of *Frullania dilatata* was found, on the same ash bole (1992 survey). This suggests that a toxic stream of SO_2-laden air must still be passing over The Wick from Colchester when the wind is from the north. A visit in the spring may well add additional bryophytes to the list however, as often some of the more sensitive species will temporarily establish themselves during a lull in the acid rain, and then rapidly disappear.

Most of the once largely open gravel workings are now blanketed with trees and shrubs which blot out the light and suck up water so that few bryophytes or even higher plants of interest now occur over much of the reserve. In addition to the regular use of a bulldozer to regenerate gravel pit features and to rejuvenate overgrown hollows, management intervention could include the judicious use of a biodegradable herbicide to clear *Crassula* around pools and winter-wet hollows. The superb lichen/ *Dicranum* moss heath on the upper beach must be kept clear of gorse and bramble: ideally it should also be enlarged. There are few 'rock' habitats at The Wick for bryophytes other than the concrete bunkers, and the old farmyard wall at one side of the car park. Scrub should be cleared from the base of the former to benefit species needing damp and light. The top of the crumbling old farmyard wall should continue to be repaired with lime-based mortar.

Ken Adams

Polytrichum juniperinum moss flourishes on the acid, rabbit-cropped heath.

Fungi

The fungi perform wonders of recycling – a vital activity that transforms a dead or dying generation into something usable for generations yet to come. Their unseen activity is ceaseless. Unless they are tasty or well known, most people are oblivious to fungi. It takes a dedicated expert like Ian Rose to capture their magic in a way that is fun and informative to the public. I am grateful to Ian for his report.

The worked-out gravel pits and the natural colonisation of the area by mainly self-sown trees and shrubs, plus planted pines, have produced a diverse habitat for fungi. The soil is light, and while in a damp year an autumn fungus foray can easily produce a list of 100 or more species, a dry year such as 2003 could produce as little as a dozen and be considered a triumph. As natural succession continues and trees mature and fall, the habitat will become more diverse and new species for the site will be identified. The very nature of the dust-like spore reproduction system of fungi ensures the area is swamped by spores just waiting for the right conditions to germinate and fulfil their purpose in nature of breaking down organic matter for reuse by the environment.

Whilst a good survey of the plants in an area can be done over two years, it is thought that due to the transient nature of fungi and unreliable fruiting, a comparable survey of the fungi might need to be carried out over 30 years. There will always be surprises in store. The following looks at some of the species found in various families:

Agaricus: The mushroom that everyone recognises, or thinks they do; the family includes the edible field (*A. campestris*), horse (*A. arvensis*) and wood mushrooms (*A. silvicola*), plus the deceptive yellow stainer (*A. xanthodermus*) which is poisonous to some people and will ruin any meal.

Amanita: This family contains some of the most poisonous species. A few are edible, but with great care and expert knowledge only. My advice to people on a foray is 'do not try'. Present at The Wick are: fly agaric (*A. muscaria*), the blusher (*A. rubescens*), the grisette (*A. fulva*), false death cap (*A. citrina*), and true death cap (*A. phalloides*).

Armillaria: The honey fungus (*A. mellea*) is almost universal. It has a reputation for killing trees. It always grows on wood and roots.

Auricularia: Jew's ear (*A. auricula-judae*) is found on dead elder branches. Fat and juicy in damp weather, it shrinks to a black crust in dry times.

Boletus: The cep or penny bun (*B. edulus*) is the prize of any foray. It is found on the reserve, together with the red cracking bolete (*B. chrysenteron*), the bay bolete (*B. dadius*), and the very hot *B. piperatus*.

Clitocybe: Seven of the funnel caps have been found, including *C. clavipes*, *C. nebularis*, *C. odora* and *C. rivulosa*.

Coprinus: Six species of ink cap include the common ink cap (*C. atramentarius*), lawyer's wig (*C. comatus*), and Japanese umbrella (*C. plicatilis*).

Hygrophoropsis: The false chanterelle is common (*H. aurantiaca*).

Laccaria: The amethyst (*L. amethystina*) and the deceiver (*L. laccata*) are both very common.

Lactarius: Well represented; about seven species are present including *L. glyciosmus*, *L. turpis*, *L. pubescens* and *L. controversus*.

Lepiota: The two large parasols are present; field parasol (*L. procera*) and shaggy parasol (*L. rachodes*), with the smaller *L. castanea*.

Lycoperdon: Three species of puffball have been found; *L. perlatum*, *L. pyriforme* and *L. molle*.

Mycena: Eight species of these small and delicate fungi have been found. *M. alcalina* smells of bleach, whilst *M. galopus* produces white droplets from the broken stipe.

Russula: Six species have been found. They are often specific to a particular host tree, and often brightly coloured.

Bracket fungi: A range of bracket fungi was found. In dry weather with few fungi in evidence, they still form fruit bodies by drawing moisture from their host logs and stumps. They include candle snuff (*Xylaria hypoxylon*), many-zoned bracket (*Coriolus versicolor*), blushing bracket (*Daedaleopsis confragosa*) and birch polypore (*Piptoporus betulinus*).

Ian Rose

Lawyer's wig toadstools, sometimes known as shaggy ink cap, are fascinating, especially to school groups.

Lichens

The old farm wall that once surrounded the Wick Farm stockyard has seen better days. Faced with flints held together with a lime-based mortar, the surviving fragments of wall remain a fine habitat for lichens. Elsewhere in the reserve, good lichen habitats are a direct legacy of decades of gravel pit turmoil, which bequeathed man-made features not present in the earlier Wick Farm. John Skinner is the County Recorder for lichens, and has contributed the following report.

The following comments and list are based on two visits during 1976. At that time, air pollution in Essex, even in this comparatively rural area, was much more than it is today. A modern survey would undoubtedly uncover a richer flora on the bark of trees because of this improvement. On the other hand, the reserve is considerably more overgrown than it was in 1976 and this will probably have caused a reduction in the extent of the terricolous (ground) lichen flora. Unfortunately, time has not permitted a recent update of the 1976 survey and a potentially interesting study remains to be done.

Sandy ground

Sandy areas, with varying amounts of gravel and of scrub cover, make up a considerable part of the reserve. Where higher plants have not gained too strong a hold the lichen flora is rich and interesting. Twenty-six species of lichen were found in this habitat in 1976, including sixteen species of

Cladonia. In places, a mat of lichens is formed, dominated by *Cladonia furcata* and *C. rangiformis*, with lesser amounts of such interesting species as *C. coccifera*, *C. foliacea*, *C. glauca*, *C. pityrea*, *C. scabriuscula* and *C. cervicornis* subsp. *verticillata*. Apart from species of *Cladonia*, other lichens found were *Hypogymnia physodes* and *Peltigera lactucifolia*, both of which were well developed on paths through the 'hawthorn wilderness'.

Small flint pebbles bore a flora of *Scoliciosporum umbrina*, *Catillaria chalybeia*, *Lecanora conizaeoides*, *Micarea erratica*, *Porpidia. soredizodes* and *Rhizocarpon reductum*. In view of the sandy ground in the reserve, this is the most likely habitat in which new additions to the species list could be discovered, particularly terricolous species of *Bacidia* and *Micarea* and possibly *Cladonia cariosa*, a lichen of dunes in eastern England.

Concrete

Twenty-three species were recorded from concrete on the reserve, twelve of which were confined to this habitat. *Lecanora dispersa* and *Caloplaca citrina*, both extremely common in Essex, dominate most concrete surfaces, but a rich flora had developed on the old bunkers, with five species of *Physcia*, *Caloplaca saxicola* and *Buellia aethalea* (normally a lichen of siliceous substrates). Shaded concrete bears *Lecania erisybe*, *Verrucaria duforii*, *V. muralis* and *V. viridula*, the latter forming large iron-stained patches on a buttress.

Old walls

The reserve is particularly fortunate in possessing some old brick walls around the public car park near the Visitor Centre. In Essex such walls are the habitat of several lichen species that are characteristic of siliceous rocks in other parts of Britain, several of which seem unable to colonise more recent brick walls. In addition the crumbly, lime-rich mortar is another important lichen habitat. The old walls near the Centre bore 26 lichen species, of which thirteen are confined to this habitat. On the bricks are *Parmelia sulcata, Lecanora intricata, L. muralist Lecidea fuscoatra,* and *Trapelia coarctata.* The crumbly mortar bears *Collema tenax, Sarcogyne regularis* and *Verrucaria muralis. Xanthoria calcicola* and *X. parietina* are conspicuous on these walls, as is *Psilolechia lucida* in shaded areas. Particularly interesting finds were *Physcia dubia* and *Hyperphyscia adglutinata.*

Corticolous (bark) lichens

Seventeen species of lichen were found on bark but a modern survey would almost certainly increase this figure considerably.

Many gorse and scrub willows were covered in *Lecanora conizaeoides,* a pollution-tolerant lichen that was abundant throughout Essex but is now becoming somewhat less common. *Lepraria incana* and *Lecanora expallens* were also found but less frequently. The more interesting species were found on some fairly small elms near the old hawthorn hedge and in particular on some willows that overhung the western side of the Bunkhouse pond. These latter trees bore 4 species of *Parmelia,* including *P. subrudecta* (uncommon in Essex in 1976, now quite common), *Xanthoria polycarpa, Evernia prunastri* and *Ramalina farinacea,* all noteworthy in 1976 but now common in many parts of the county.

Few interesting species were seen on dead wood, although old fence posts at the southern end of the reserve which were not examined may carry lichens. *Lecanora conizaeoides, L. dispersa* agg., *L. expallens* and *Placynthiella icmalea* were all seen on old railway sleepers used as seats.

John Skinner

Midwinter is an endurance test for wildlife
Midsummer: living is easy for this community of badgers. *Photograph: Don Hunford*

The Wildlife of Fingringhoe Wick

A list of flora and fauna species recorded in the nature reserve 1961-2004

PLANTS
* no longer present

BRYOPHYTA

HEPATICAE
LIVERWORTS
Blasia pusilla* — Common Kettlewort
Cephaloziella divaricata — Common Threadwort
Frullania dilatata — Common Threadwort
Lophocolea bidentata — Bifid Crestwort
Lophocolea heterophylla — Variable-leaved Crestwort
Lophocolea semiteres — Southern Crestwort [alien]
Lophozia excisa — Capitate Notchwort
Marchantia polymorpha — Common Liver-green
Metzgeria furcata — Forked Veilwort
Riccia fluitans — Floating Crystalwort

ANTHOCEROTAE
HORNWORTS
Anthoceros agrestis* — Field Hornwort

MUSCI
MOSSES
Amblystegium serpens — Creeping Feather-moss
Atrichum undulatum — Common Smoothcap
Aulacomnium androgynum — Bud-headed Groove-moss
Aulacomnium palustre — Bog Groove-moss
Barbula convoluta — Lesser Bird's-claw Beard-moss
Barbula unguiculata — Bird's-claw Beard-moss
Brachythecium albicans — Whitish Feather-moss
Brachythecium rivulare — River Feather-moss
Brachythecium rutabulum — Rough-stalked Feather-moss
Brachythecium velutinum — Velvet Feather-moss
Bryoerthyrophyllum recurvirostrum — Red Beard-moss
Bryum algovicum rutheanum — Drooping Thread-moss
Bryum argenteum — Silver-moss
Bryum caespiticium — Tufted Thread-moss
Bryum capillare var. capillare — Capillary Thread-moss
Bryum dichotomum — Bicoloured Bryum
Bryum gemmiferum — Small-bud Bryum
Bryum imbricatum — Small-mouthed Thread-moss
Bryum knowltonii* — Knowlton's Thread-moss
Bryum pallens — Pale Thread-moss

Bryum pseudotriquetrum — Marsh Bryum
Bryum rubens — Crimson-tuber Thread-moss
Calliergon cordifolium* — Heart-leaved Spear-moss
Calliergonella cuspidata — Pointed Spear-moss
Campylopus introflexus — Heath Star Moss [alien]
Ceratodon purpureus — Redshank
Dicranella heteromalla — Silky Forklet-moss
Dicranella schreberiana — Schreber's Forklet-moss
Dicranella staphylina — Field Forklet-moss
Dicranella varia — Variable Forklet-moss
Dicranoweisia cirrata — Common Pincushion
Dicranum scoparium — Broom Fork-moss
Didymodon insulanus — Cylindric Beard-moss
Didymodon vinealis — Soft-tufted Beard-moss
Drepanocladus aduncus — Kneiff's Hook-moss
Fissidens bryoides — Lesser Pocket-moss
Fissidens exilis — Slender Pocket-moss
Fissidens incurvus — Short-leaved Pocket-moss
Fissidens taxifolius var. taxifolius — Common Pocket-moss
Funaria hygrometrica — Common Cord-moss
Grimmia pulvinata — Grey-cushioned Grimmia
Homalothecium sericeum — Silky Wall Feather-moss
Hypnum cupressiforme sens. str. — Cypress-leaved Plait-moss
Hypnum jutlandicum — Heath Plait-moss
Hypnum lacunosum var. lacunosum — Great Plait-moss
Hypnum resupinatum — Supine Plait-moss
Kindbergia praelonga — Common Feather-moss
Leptodictyum riparium — Kneiff's Feather-moss
Mnium hornum — Swan's-neck Thyme-moss
Orthodontium lineare — Cape Thread-moss [alien]
Orthotrichum affine — Wood Bristle-moss
Orthotrichum anomalum — Anomalous Bristle-moss
Orthotrichum diaphanum — White-tipped Bristle-moss
Orthotrichum lyellii — Lyell's Bristle-moss
Oxyrrhynchium hyans — Swartz's Feather-moss
Phascum cuspidatum var. cuspidatum — Cuspidate Earth-moss
Philonotis fontana* — Fountain Apple-moss

Plagiothecium curvifolium	Curved Silk-moss
Plagiothecium denticulatum var. denticulatum	Dented Silk-moss
Plagiothecium undulatum	Waved Silk-moss
Pleuridium acuminatum	Taper-leaved Earth-moss
Pleurozium schreberi*	Red-stemmed Feather-moss
Pogonatum aloides*	Aloe Haircap
Pohlia annotina	Pale-fruited Thread-Moss
Pohlia nutans	Nodding Thread-moss
Polytrichastrum formosum	Bank Haircap
Polytrichum commune*	Common Haircap
Polytrichum juniperinum	Juniper Haircap
Polytrichum piliferum	Bristly Haircap
Pseudocrossidium hornschuchianum	Hornschuch's Beard-moss
Pseudoscleropodium purum	Neat Feather-moss
Rhynchostegium confertum	Clustered Feather-moss
Rhytidiadelphus squarrosus	Springy Turf-moss
Rhytidiadelphus triquetrus*	Big Shaggy-moss
Schistidium crassipilum	Thick-point Grimmia
Sphagnum fallax*	Flat-topped Bog-moss
Sphagnum fimbriatum*	Fringed Bog-moss
Sphagnum palustre var. palustre*	Blunt-leaved Bog-moss
Sphagnum squarrosum	Spiky Bog-moss
Sphagnum subnitens*	Lustrous Bog-moss
Thuidium tamariscinum	Common Tamarisk-moss
Tortula truncata	Common Pottia
Syntrichia intermedia	Intermediate Screw-moss
Syntrichia latifolia	Water Screw-moss
Syntrichia ruralis var. ruralis	Great Hairy Screw-moss
Tortula muralis	Wall Screw-moss
Trichodon cylindricus	Cylindric Ditrichum
Zygodon viridissimus	Green Yoke-moss

PTERIDOPHYTA — FERNS & FERN ALLIES

Asplenium adiantum-nigrum sens.lat.	Black Spleenwort
Athyrium filix-femina	Lady Fern
Azolla filiculoides	Water Fern
Blechnum spicant*	Hard Fern
Dryopteris affinis affinis	Scaly Male Fern
Dryopteris carthusiana	Narrow Buckler-Fern
Dryopteris dilatata	Broad Buckler-Fern
Dryopteris filix-mas	Male Fern
Equisetum arvense	Field Horsetail
Equisetum palustre	Marsh Horsetail
Lycopodium clavatum*	Stag's-Horn Clubmoss
Ophioglossum vulgatum	Adder's Tongue
Osmunda regalis*	Royal Fern
Phyllitis scolopendrium	Hart's-Tongue
Polypodium vulgare agg.	Common Polypody
Polystichum aculeatum	Hard Shield-Fern
Polystichum setiferum	Soft Shield-Fern
Pteridium aquilinum	Bracken

PINOPSIDA

Larix decidua	Larch [planted]
Pinus sylvestris	Scots Pine [planted]
Taxus baccata	Yew [bird sown]

MAGNOLI-OPSIDA

Acer campestre	Field Maple
Achillea millefolium	Yarrow
Aesculus hippocastanum	Horse-Chestnut
Aethusa cynapium	Fool's Parsley
Agrimonia eupatoria	Agrimony
Agrostis capillaris	Common Bent
Agrostis gigantea	Black Bent
Agrostis stolonifera	Creeping Bent
Aira caryophyllea	Silver Hair-Grass
Aira praecox	Early Hair-Grass
Ajuga reptans	Bugle
Alisma plantago-aquatica	Water-Plantain
Alnus glutinosa	Alder
Alopecurus geniculatus	Marsh Foxtail
Alopecurus myosuroides	Black-Grass
Alopecurus pratensis	Meadow Foxtail
Anagallis arvensis spp. arvensis	Scarlet Pimpernel
Anchusa arvensis	Bugloss
Angelica sylvestris	Wild Angelica

Anisantha sterilis	Barren Brome	*Carduus nutans*	Musk Thistle
Anthoxanthum odoratum	Sweet Vernal Grass	*Carduus tenuiflorus*	Slender Thistle
Anthriscus caucalis	Bur Parsley	*Carex divisa*	Divided Sedge
Anthriscus sylvestris	Cow Parsley	*Carex divulsa divulsa* ssp.	Grey Sedge
Aphanes arvensis agg.	Parsley Piert	*Carex hirta*	Hairy Sedge
Apium nodiflorum	Fool's Water-Cress	*Carex muricata* ssp. *lamprocarpa*	Prickly Sedge
Arabidopsis thaliana	Thale Cress	*Carex otrubae*	False Fox-Sedge
Arctium minus minus	Lesser Burdock	*Carex ovalis*	Oval Sedge
Arenaria serpyllifolia ssp. *leptoclados*	Small Thyme-Leaved Sandwort	*Carex paniculata*	Greater Tussock-Sedge
Armeria maritima ssp. *maritima*	Thrift	*Carex remota*	Remote Sedge
Arrhenatherum elatius	False Oat-Grass	*Carpinus betulus*	Hornbeam
*Artemisia absinthium**	Wormwood	*Castanea sativa*	Sweet Chestnut
Artemisia vulgaris	Mugwort	*Centaurea calcitrapa**	Red Star-Thistle
Arum maculatum	Lords-And-Ladies	*Centaurea nigra*	Common Knapweed
Aster tripolium	Sea Aster	*Centaurium erythraea*	Common Centaury
Atriplex littoralis	Grass-Leaved Orache	*Cerastium diffusum*	Sea Mouse-ear
Atriplex patula	Common Orache	*Cerastium fontanum*	Common Mouse-Ear
Atriplex portulacoides	Sea Purslane	*Cerastium glomeratum*	Sticky Mouse-Ear
Atriplex prostrata	Spear-Leaved Orache	*Ceratophyllum demersum*	Rigid Hornwort
Avena fatua	Wild Oat	*Ceratophyllum submersum*	Soft Hornwort
Ballota nigra	Black Horehound		
Barbarea vulgaris	Winter-Cress	*Chaerophyllum temulum*	Rough Chervil
Bellis perennis	Daisy	*Chenopodium album* agg.	Fat Hen
Betula pendula	Silver Birch	*Cirsium arvense*	Creeping Thistle
Betula pubescens	Downy Birch	*Cirsium palustre*	Marsh Thistle
*Blackstonia perfoliata**	Yellow Wort	*Cirsium vulgare*	Spear Thistle
Bolboschoenus maritimus	Sea Club-Rush	*Claytonia perfoliata*	Spring Beauty
Bromopsis ramosa	Hairy Brome	*Clematis vitalba*	Traveller's Joy
Bromus commutatus	Meadow Brome	*Clinopodium calamintha*	Lesser Calamint
Bromus hordeaceus	Soft Brome	*Cochlearia anglica*	English Scurvygrass
Bryonia dioica	White Bryony	*Conium maculatum*	Hemlock
Buddleja davidii	Butterfly-Bush	*Conopodium majus*	Pignut
*Bupleurum tenuissimum**	Slender Hare's-Ear	*Convolvulus arvensis*	Field Bindweed
Calamagrostis epigejos	Wood Small-reed	*Conyza canadensis*	Canadian Fleabane
Calluna vulgaris	Heather [introduced]	*Conyza sumatrensis*	Guernsey Fleabane
Calystegia sepium ssp. *sepium*	Great Bindweed	*Cornus sanguinea*	Dogwood
Calystegia soldanella	Sea Bindweed	*Coronopus squamatus*	Swine-Cress
Capsella bursa-pastoris	Shepherd's-Purse	*Corylus avellana*	Hazel
Cardamine hirsuta	Hairy Bitter-Cress	*Crambe maritima*	Sea-Kale
Cardamine pratensis	Cuckooflower	*Crassula helmsii*	New Zealand Pigmyweed
Carduus crispus	Welted Thistle		

Crataegus monogyna	Hawthorn	*Galium mollugo*	Hedge Bedstraw
Crataegus x macrocarpa	Hybrid Hawthorn	*Galium palustre* ssp. *palustre*	Common Marsh-Bedstraw
Crepis capillaris	Smooth Hawk's-Beard	*Galium saxatile**	Heath Bedstraw
Cynosurus cristatus	Crested Dog's-Tail	*Galium verum*	Lady's Bedstraw
Cytisus scoparius	Broom	*Geranium dissectum*	Cut-Leaved Crane's-Bill
Dactylis glomerata	Cock's-Foot	*Geranium molle*	Dove's-Foot Crane's-Bill
Dactylorhiza fuchsii	Common Spotted-Orchid	*Geranium robertianum*	Herb-Robert
Digitalis purpurea	Foxglove	*Glaux maritime*	Sea-Milkwort
Echium vulgare	Viper's Bugloss	*Glechoma hederacea*	Ground-Ivy
Eleocharis palustris agg.	Common Spike-Rush	*Glyceria fluitans*	Floating Sweet-Grass
Elodea nuttallii	Nuttall's Water-Weed	*Glyceria maxima*	Reed Sweet-Grass
Elytrigia atherica var. *antherica*	Sea Couch	*Gnaphalium uliginosum*	Marsh Cudweed
Elytrigia juncea	Sand Couch	*Hedera helix*	Ivy
Elytrigia repens	Common Couch	*Heracleum sphondylium*	Hogweed
Epilobium ciliatum	American Willowherb	*Hieracium umbellatum*	a Hawkweed
Epilobium hirsutum	Great Willowherb	*Holcus lanatus*	Yorkshire-Fog
Epilobium montanum	Broad-Leaved Willowherb	*Holcus mollis*	Creeping Soft-Grass
Epilobium obscurum	Short-fruited Willowherb	*Honckenya peploides*	Sea Sandwort
Epilobium roseum	Pale Willowherb	*Hordeum murinum*	Wall Barley
Erica cinerea	Bell Heather [introduced]	*Hordeum secalinum*	Meadow Barley
Erigeron acer	Blue Fleabane	*Humulus lupulus*	Hop
Erodium cicutarium sens.str.	Common Stork's-Bill	*Hyacinthoides non-scripta*	Bluebell
Erophila verna sens. stace	Common Whitlowgrass	*Hypericum humifusum*	Trailing St. John's-Wort
Euonymus europaeus	Spindle	*Hypericum perforatum*	Perforate St. John's-Wort
Euphorbia helioscopia	Sun Spurge	*Hypericum pulchrum*	Slender St. John's-Wort
Fagus sylvatica	Beech [planted]	*Hypericum tetrapterum*	Square-Stalked St. John's-Wort
Fallopia convolvulus	Black Bindweed	*Hypochaeris radicata*	Cat's-Ear
Festuca arundinacea	Tall Fescue	*Ilex aquifolium*	Holly
Festuca filiformis	Fine-Leaved Sheep's-Fescue	*Iris pseudacorus*	Yellow Iris
Festuca gigantea	Giant Fescue	*Isolepis setacea*	Bristle Club-Rush
Festuca rubra sens.str.	Red Fescue	*Juncus articulatus*	Jointed Rush
Filago minima	Small Cudweed	*Juncus bufonius* agg.	Toad Rush agg.
Filago vulgaris	Common Cudweed	*Juncus effusus*	Soft Rush
Filipendula ulmaria	Meadowsweet	*Juncus gerardii*	Saltmarsh Rush
Fraxinus excelsior	Ash	*Juncus inflexus*	Hard Rush
Fumaria officinalis ssp. *officinalis*	Common Fumitory	*Juncus maritimus*	Sea Rush
Fumaria officinalis wirtgenii ssp.	Common Fumitory	*Juncus subnodulosus*	Blunt-Flowered Rush
Galeopsis tetrahit	Common Hemp-Nettle	*Kickxia elatine*	Sharp-Leaved Fluellen
Galium aparine	Cleavers	*Knautia arvensis*	Field Scabious
		Lactuca serriola	Prickly Lettuce
		Lactuca virosa	Greater Lettuce
		Lamium album	White Dead-Nettle

Lamium amplexicaule	Hen-Bit Dead-Nettle
Lamium purpureum	Red Dead-Nettle
Lapsana communis	Nipplewort
Lathyrus nissolia	Grass Vetchling
Lathyrus pratensis	Meadow Vetchling
Lemna minor	Common Duckweed
Lemna minuta	Least Duckweed [alien]
Lemna trisulca	Ivy-Leaved Duckweed
Leontodon autumnalis	Autumnal Hawkbit
Lepidium heterophyllum	Smith's Pepperwort
Lepidium latifolium	Dittander
Leucanthemum vulgare	Oxeye Daisy
Limonium vulgare	Common Sea-Lavender
Lolium multiflorum	Italian Rye-Grass
Lolium perenne	Perennial Rye-Grass
Lonicera periclymenum	Honeysuckle
Lotus corniculatus	Common Bird's-Foot-Trefoil
Lotus pedunculatus	Large Bird's-Foot-Trefoil
Luzula campestris	Field Wood-Rush
Luzula multiflora ssp. *congesta*	Heath Wood-Rush
Luzula multiflora ssp. *multiflora*	Heath Wood-Rush
Lycopus europaeus	Gipsywort
Malva neglecta	Dwarf Mallow
Malva sylvestris	Common Mallow
Matricaria discoidea	Pineapple Weed
Medicago arabica	Spotted Medick
Medicago lupulina	Black Medick
Mentha aquatica	Water Mint
Mercurialis perennis	Dog's Mercury
Moehringia trinervia	Three-Nerved Sandwort
Montia fontana agg.	Blinks
Myosotis arvensis	Field Forget-Me-Not
Myosotis discolor	Changing Forget-Me-Not
Myosotis laxa ssp. *caespitosa*	Tufted Forget-Me-Not
Myosotis ramosissima	Early Forget-Me-Not
Myosurus minimus	Mousetail
Myriophyllum spicatum	Spiked Water-Milfoil
Oenanthe crocata	Hemlock Water-Dropwort
Oenothera biennis	Common Evening-Primrose
Ononis spinosa	Spiny Restharrow
Onopordum acanthium	Cotton Thistle
Ophrys apifera	Bee Orchid
Ornithopus perpusillus	Bird's-Foot
Orobanche minor	Common Broomrape
Papaver rhoeas	Common Poppy
Persicaria hydropiper	Water-Pepper
Persicaria maculosa	Redshank
Phalaris canariensis	Canary-Grass
Phleum bertolonii	Smaller Cat's-Tail
Phleum pratense sens.str.	Timothy
Phragmites australis	Common Reed
Picris echioides	Bristly Oxtongue
Pilosella officinarum	Mouse-Ear-Hawkweed
Plantago coronopus	Buck's-Horn Plantain
Plantago lanceolata	Ribwort Plantain
Plantago major	Greater Plantain
Plantago maritima	Sea Plantain
Poa annua	Annual Meadow-Grass
Poa humilis	Spreading Meadow-Grass
Poa pratensis sens.lat.	Smooth Meadow-Grass
Poa trivialis	Rough Meadow-Grass
Polygonum aviculare sens.str.	Knotgrass
Populus alba	White Poplar
Populus nigra var. *'Italica'*	Lombardy-Poplar [planted]
Populus tremula	Aspen
*Potamogeton berchtoldii**	Small Pondweed
Potamogeton crispus	Curled Pondweed
Potamogeton pectinatus	Fennel Pondweed
Potentilla argentea	Hoary Cinquefoil
Potentilla erecta	Tormentil
*Potentilla recta**	Sulphur Cinquefoil
Potentilla reptans	Creeping Cinquefoil
Potentilla sterilis	Barren Strawberry
Prunella vulgaris	Selfheal
Prunus spinosa	Blackthorn
Puccinellia maritima	Common Saltmarsh-Grass
Pulicaria dysenterica	Common Fleabane
Pyrola rotundifolia ssp. *rotundifolia*	Round-Leaved Wintergreen
Quercus cerris	Turkey Oak

Small-flowered
Cranesbill or
Dovesfoot
Cranesbill?

Quercus ilex	Evergreen Oak	*Rumex maritimus*	Golden Dock
Quercus robur	Pedunculate Oak	*Rumex obtusifolius*	Broad-Leaved Dock
Ranunculus acris	Meadow Buttercup	*Sagina procumbens*	Procumbent Pearlwort
Ranunculus baudotii	Brackish Water-Crowfoot	*Salicornia* agg.	Glasswort
Ranunculus bulbosus	Bulbous Buttercup	*Salix caprea*	Goat Willow
Ranunculus circinatus	Fan-Leaved Water-Crowfoot	*Salix cinerea* ssp. *cinerea*	Willow
Ranunculus ficaria ssp. *ficaria*	Lesser Celandine	*Salix fragilis*	Crack Willow
		Salix repens	Dwarf Willow
Ranunculus flammula	Lesser Spearwort	*Salix viminalis*	Osier
Ranunculus lingua	Greater Spearwort [planted]	*Salix x sepulcralis* nothovar. *chrysocoma*	Weeping Willow [planted]
Ranunculus peltatus	Pond Water-crowfoot	*Sambucus nigra*	Elder
Ranunculus repens	Creeping Buttercup	*Samolus valerandi**	Brookweed
Ranunculus sceleratus	Celery-Leaved Buttercup	*Sarcocornia perennis*	Perennial Glasswort
Reseda luteola	Weld	*Schoenoplectus lacustris*	Common Club-Rush
Rosa arvensis	Field Rose	*Scleranthus annuus*	Annual Knawel
Rosa canina agg.	Dog Rose	*Scrophularia nodosa*	Common Figwort
Rubus fruticosus agg.	Bramble	*Senecio erucifolius*	Hoary Ragwort
Rubus macrophyllus	Bramble	*Senecio jacobaea*	Common Ragwort
Rubus ulmifolius	Bramble	*Senecio squalidus*	Oxford Ragwort
Rumex acetosa	Common Sorrel	*Senecio viscosus*	Sticky Groundsel
Rumex acetosella ssp. *acetosella*	Sheep's Sorrel	*Senecio vulgaris*	Groundsel
		Seriphidium maritimum	Sea Wormwood
Rumex crispus	Curled Dock	*Sherardia arvensis*	Field Madder

Silene dioica	Red Campion
Silene latifolia	White Campion
*Silybum marianum**	Milk Thistle
Sison amomum	Stone Parsley
Sisymbrium officinale	Hedge Mustard
Solanum dulcamara	Bittersweet
Solanum nigrum	Black Nightshade
Sonchus arvensis	Perennial Sow-Thistle
Sonchus oleraceus	Smooth Sow-Thistle
Sonchus palustris	Marsh Sow-Thistle [introduced]
Sorbus aria agg.	Whitebeam [planted]
Sorbus aucuparia	Rowan
Sparganium erectum ssp. *erectum*	Branched Bur-Reed
Spartina anglica	Common Cord-Grass
Spartina maritima	Small Cord-Grass
Spergula arvensis	Corn Spurrey
Spergularia media	Greater Sea-Spurrey
Spergularia rubra	Sand Spurrey
Stachys palustris	Marsh Woundwort
Stachys sylvatica	Hedge Woundwort
Stellaria graminea	Lesser Stitchwort
Stellaria holostea	Greater Stitchwort
Stellaria holostea	Greater Stitchwort
Stellaria media	Common Chickweed
Stellaria pallida	Lesser Chickweed
Stellaria uliginosa	Bog Stitchwort
Suaeda maritima	Annual Sea-Blite
Suaeda vera	Shrubby Seablite
Tamus communis	Black Bryony
Taraxacum officinale agg.	Dandelion
Thlaspe arvense	Field Penny-cress
Torilis japonica	Upright Hedge-parsley
Tragopogon pratense ssp. *minor*	Goatsbeard
Trifolium arvense	Hare's-foot Clover
Trifolium campestre	Hop Trefoil
Trifolium glomeratum	Clustered Clover
Trifolium micranthum	Slender Trefoil
Trifolium ornithopioides	Bird's-foot Clover
Trifolium pratense	Red Clover
Trifolium repens	White Clover
Trifolium striatum	Knotted Clover
Triglochin maritima	Sea Arrow-grass
Trisetum flavascens	Yellow Oat-grass
Typha latifolia	Greater Reedmace
Ulex europaeus	Gorse
Ulmus procera	English Elm
Urtica dioica	Common Nettle
Urtica urens	Small Nettle
Veronica arvensis	Wall Speedwell
Veronica chamaedrys	Germander Speedwell
Veronica hederifolia ssp. *hederifolia*	Ivy-Leaved Speedwell
Veronica officinalis	Heath Speedwell
Veronica persica	Common Field Speedwell
Veronica serpyllifolia ssp. *serpyllifolia*	Thyme-Leaved Speedwell
Vicia cracca	Tufted Vetch
Vicia hirsuta	Hairy Tare
Vicia sativa ssp. *nigra*	Narrow-Leaved Vetch
Vicia sativa ssp. *sativa*	Common Vetch
Vicia tetrasperma	Smooth Tare
Viola arvensis	Field Pansy
Viola riviniana	Common Dog-Violet
Vulpia bromoides	Squirrel-Tail Fescue

FUNGI
ASCOMYCOTA

		FLASK FUNGI
Aleuria aurantia	Orange-Peel Fungus
Chlorociboria aeruginascens	Green Elfcup
Diatrype disciformis	Beech Barkspot
Epichloë typhina	Choke
Erysiphe urticae	
Geopora septula	
Hypoxylon fragiforme	Beech Woodwart
Hypoxylon multiforme	Birch Woodwart
Microsphaera alphitoides	
Nectria cinnabarina	Coral-Spot Fungus
Peziza badia	Bay Cup
Rustroemia firma	Brown Cap
Xylaria hypoxylon	Candlesnuff
Xylaria multiforme	Birch Woodwort
Xylaria polymorpha	Dead Man`s Fingers

BASIDIOMYCOTA

HETEROBASIDIO-MYCETES

Auricularia auricula-judae	Jew`s Ear
Calocera cornea	Small Stagshorn
Dacrymyces stillatus	Common Jellyspot
Tremella foliacea	Yellow Brain
Tremella mesenterica	Golden Jelly Fungus

APHYLLOPHORALES — NON-GILLED FUNGI

Cantharellus ferruginascens	
Chondrostereum purpureum	Silverleaf Fungus
Clavulina cinerea	Grey Coral
Clavulina cristata	
Daedalea quercina	Oak Mazegill
Daedaleopsis confragosa	Blushing Bracket
Fistulina hepatica	Beef-Steak Fungus
Lenzites betulinus	Birch Mazegill
Meripilus giganteus	Giant Polypore
Piptoporus betulinus	Birch Polypore
Polyporus squamosus	Dryad`s Saddle
Polyporus leptocephalus	Blackfoot Polyore
Ramaria stricta	Upright Coral
Phlebia radiata	Wrinkled Crust
Stereum hirsutum	Hairy Curtain Crust
Thelephora terrestris	Earth-Fan
Trametes gibbosa	Lumpy Bracket
Trametes versicolor	Turkeytail
Trichaptum abietinum	Purplepore Bracket

BOLETALES — BOLETES

Boletus badius	Bay Bolete
Boletus edulis	Cep
Chalciporus piperatus	Peppery Bolete
Chroogomphus rutilus	Coppery Spike-Cap
Hygrophoropsis aurantiaca	False Chanterelle
Leccinum molle	
Leccinum roseofractum	Blushing Bolete
Leccinum scabrum	Brown Birch-Bolete
Leccinum umbrionoides	
Leccinum variicolor	Mottled Bolete
Leccinum versipelle	Orange Birch-Bolete
Paxillus involutus	Brown Roll-Rim
Suillus grevillei	Larch Bolete
Suillus luteus	Slippery Jack
Tapienella panuoides	Oyster Roll Rim
Xerocomus chrysenteron	Red-Cracking Bolete

AGARICALES — AGARICS

Agaricus arvensis	Horse Mushroom
Agaricus campestris	Field Mushroom
Agaricus comtulus	
Agaricus impudicus	
Agaricus macrosporus	
Agaricus silvaticus	Blushing Wood Mushroom
Agaricus silvicola	Wood Mushroom
Agaricus xanthodermus	Yellow Stainer
Agrocybe cylindracea	Poplar Fieldcap
Amanita citrina	False Deathcap
Amanita fulva	Tawny Grisette
Amanita muscaria	Fly Agaric
Amanita rubescens	Blusher
Amanita vaginata	Grisette
Armillaria mellea	Honey Fungus
Bolbitius vitellina	Yellow Fieldcap
Calyptella capula	
Clitocybe clavipes	Club Foot
Clitocybe fragrans	Fragrant Funnel
Clitocybe geotropa	Trooping Funnel
Clitocybe gibba	Common Funnel Cap
Clitocybe nebularis	Clouded Agaric
Clitocybe odora	Aniseed Toadstool
Clitocybe phyllophila	Frosty Funnel
Clitocybe rivulosa	Fool's Funnel
Clitocybe vibecina	Mealy Funnel
Clitopilus prunulus	
Collybia butyracea	Butter Cap
Collybia dryophila	Russet Tough-Shank
Collybia maculata	Spotted Tough-Shank
Collybia peronata	Wood Woolly-Foot
Conocybe filaris	Fool's Cone-cap
Conocybe tenera	Brown Cone-Cap
Coprinus atramentarius	
Coprinus comatus	Shaggy Ink-Cap
Coprinus lagopus	Hare'sfoot Inkcap
Coprinus macrocephalus	
Coprinus micaceus	Glistening Ink-Cap

Coprinus plicatilis	Pleated Ink-cap	*Lactarius subdulcis*	Mild Milk-Cap
Coprinus silvaticus		*Lactarius torminosus*	Woolly Milk-Cap
Cortinarius alboviolaceus	Pearly Webcap	*Lactarius vietus*	Grey Milk-Cap
Cortinarius cinnamomeus	Cinnamon Webcap	*Lepiota castanea*	Chestnut Dapperling
		Lepiota cristata	Stinking Parasol
Cortinarius ochroleucus		*Lepiota oreadiformis*	
Cortinarius pseudosalor		*Lepista flaccida*	Tawny Funnel
Cortinarius purpurascens	Bruising Webcap	*Lepista nuda*	Wood Blewit
Cortinarius saniosus		*Leucoagaricus leucothites*	White Dapperling
Cortinarius trivialis	Girdled Webcap		
Crepidotus variabilis	Variable Oysterling	*Macrolepiota excoriata*	
Cystoderma amianthinum	Earthy Powdercap	*Macrolepiota procera*	Parasol
		Macrolepiota rhacodes	Shaggy Parasol
Entoloma nidorosum		*Marasmiellus ramealis*	Twig Parachute
Entoloma rhodopolium	Wood Pinkgill	*Marasmius androsaceus*	Horse-Hair Fungus
Flammulina velutipes	Velvet Shank	*Marasmius oreades*	Fairy Ring Champignon
Gymnopilus junonius	Spectacular Rustgill	*Marasmius rotula*	Collared Parachute
Gymnopilus penetrans	Common Rustgill	*Marasmius scorodonius*	
Hebeloma crustuliniforme	Poison Pie	*Micromphale inodorum*	
		Mycena aetites	Drab Bonnet
Hebeloma mesophaeum	Veiled Poison Pie	*Mycena epipterygia*	
Hebeloma pusillum		*Mycena flavescens*	
Hebeloma sinuosum		*Mycena flavoalba*	
Hygrocybe coccinea	Scarlet Hood	*Mycena galericulata*	Common bonnet
Hygrocybe conica	Conical Wax-Cap	*Mycena galopus*	Milking bonnet
Hygrocybe virginea	Snowy Wax-Cap	*Mycena inclinata*	Clustered Bonnet
Hygrophorus hypothejus	Herald Of Winter	*Mycena leptocephala*	Nitrous Bonnet
Hypholoma fasciculare	Sulphur Tuft	*Mycena polygramma*	Grooved Bonnet
Inocybe lacera	Torn Fibrecap	*Mycena pura*	Lilac Bonnet
Kuehneromyces mutabilis	Sheathed Woodtuft	*Mycena rorida*	Dripping Bonnet
		Mycena stipata	Yellowleg Bonnet
Laccaria amethystea	Amethyst Deceiver	*Mycena vitilis*	Snapping bonnet
Laccaria laccata	Deceiver	*Myxomphalia maura*	
Laccaria proxima	Scurfy Deceiver	*Omphalina ericetorum*	Heath Navel
Laccaria purpureobadia		*Omphalina oniscus*	
Lacrymaria lacrymabunda	Weeping Widow	*Panaeolus rickenii*	
		Panaeolus speciosus	
Lactarius controversus		*Panaeolus subbalteatus*	
Lactarius deliciosus	Saffron Milk-Cap	*Pholiota highlandensis*	Charcoal Pholiota
Lactarius glyciosmus	Coconut-Scented Milk-Cap	*Pholiota tuberculosa*	
		Pluteus cervinus	Fawn Pluteus
Lactarius plumbens	Ugly Milk-Cap	*Pluteus luteovirens*	
Lactarius pubescens	Bearded Milk-Cap	*Psathyrella candolleana*	Pale Brittlestem
Lactarius quietus	Oak Milk-Cap	*Psathyrella conopilus*	
Lactarius rufus	Rufous Milk-Cap		

Psathyrella piluliformis	Common Stump Brittlestem
Rickenella fibula	Orange Mosscap
Rickenella swartzii	Collared Mosscap
Russula aeruginea	Green Brittlegill
Russula atropurpurea	Purple Brittlegill
Russula betularum	Birch Brittlegill
Russula brunneoviolacea	
Russula cyanoxantha	Charcoal Burner
Russula delica	Milk-White Brittlegill
Russula emetica	Sickener
Russula fragilis	Fragile Brittlegill
Russula ochroleuca	Ochre Brittlegill
Russula sororia	Sepia Bottlegill
Russula versicolor	Variable Brittlegill
Russula xerampelina	Crab Brittlegill
Stropharia aeruginosa	Verdigris Agaric
Tricholoma fulvum	Birch Knight
Tricholoma terreum	Grey Knight
Tricholomopsis rutilans	Plums And Custard
Volvariella gloioceplata	Stubble Rosegill

GASTROMYCETES · **PUFFBALLS etc.**

Bovista dermoxantha	Dwarf Bovist
Bovista plumbea	Lead-Grey Bovist
Handkea excipuliformis	Pestle-Shaped Puffball
Handkea utriformis	Mosaic Puffball
Calvatia gigantea	Giant Puffball
Lycoperdon nigrescens	Dusky Puffball
Lycoperdon molle	Soft-Spined Puffball
Lycoperdon perlatum	Puffball
Lycoperdon pyriforme	Stump Puffball
Phallus impudicus	Stinkhorn
Scleroderma areolatum	Leopard-Spotted Earthball
Scleroderma bovista	Potato Earthball
Scleroderma citrinum	Common Earthball
Scleroderma verrucosum	Scaly Earthball
Vascellum pratense	Meadow Puffball

TELEOMYCETES · **RUSTS,SMUTS & BUNTS**

Melampsora epitea	
Phragmidium violaceum	Violet Bramble Rust

Puccinia malvacearum
Pucciniastrum epilobii
Ustilago violacea

LICHENIZED FUNGI · **LICHENS**

Acarospora fuscata
Amandinea punctata
Buellia aethalea
Caloplaca citrina sens. lat.
Caloplaca flavescens
Caloplaca holocarpa
Caloplaca saxicola
Canelariella aurella
Canelariella medians
Canelariella vitellina
Catillaria chalybeia
Cladonia cervicornis subsp. *cervicornis*
Cladonia cervicornis subsp. *verticillata*
Cladonia chlorophaea
Cladonia coccifera
Cladonia coniocraea
Cladonia. fimbriata
Cladonia. floerkeana
Cladonia foliacea
Cladonia furcata
Cladonia humilis
Cladonia glauca
Cladonia polydactyla
Cladonia ramulosa
Cladonia rangiformis
Cladonia scabriuscula
Cladonia subulata
Cliostomum griffithii
Collema tenax
Diploicia cariescens
Evernia prunastri
Hyperphyscia adglutinata
Hypogymnia physodes
Lecania erisybe
Lecanora campestris
Leconora conizaeoides

Leconora dispersa
Leconora expallens
Lecanora atra   probably extinct
Lecanora intricata
Lecanora muralis
Lecidea fuscoatra

Lecidella scabra
Lecidella stigmatea
Lepraria incana

Melanelia glabratula
Melanelia subaurifera
cf. Micarea prasina
Micarea erratica

Parmelia sulcata
Peltigera lactucifolia
Peltigera neckeri   first record 2005
Phaeophyscia nigricans
Phaeophyscia orbicularis
Physcia adscendens
Physia caesia
Physia dubia
Physia tenella
Physconia. grisea
Placynthiella icmalea
Porpidia soredizodes
Porpidia tuberculosa
Psilolechia lucida
Punctelia subrudecta
Ramalina farinacea
Rhizocarpon reductum
Rinodina genarii
Sarcogyne regularis
Scoliciosporum
umbrinum
Trapelia coarctata
Trapeliopsis. granulosa
Verrucaria duforii
Verrucaria muralis
Verrucaria nigrescens
Verrucaria viridula
Xanthoria calcicola
Xanthoria candelaria
Xanthoria parietina

Xanthoria polycarpa

ANIMALS

PLATY-HELMINTHS   **FLATWORMS**

Polycelis tenuis
Dugesia polychroa
Dugesia tigrina

MOLLUSCS   **SLUGS, SNAILS & BIVALVES**

MARINE
Abra alba
Abra tenuis
Alderia modesta
Angulus tenuis   Thin Tellin
Cerastoderma edule   Cockle
Crepidula fornicata   Slipper limpet
Lepidochitona cinerea
Limapontia depressa
Littorina littoralis   Common Periwinkle
Littorina saxatilis   Rough Periwinkle
Macoma balthica   Baltic Tellin
Mya arenaria   Sand-gaper
Mytilus edulis   Common Mussel
Ostrea edulis   European Oyster
Petricola pholadiformis   American Piddock
Scrobicularia plana   Peppery Furrow Shell
FRESH WATER / TERRESTRIAL
Aegopinella nitidula
Anisus leucostoma   Button Ramshorn
Arion circumscriptus agg.
Arion intermedius   Hedgehog Slug
Assiminea grayana   Dun Sentinell
Carychium minimum   Slender Herald Snail
Cepaea hortensis   White Lipped Snail
Cepaea nemoralis   Brown Lipped Snail
Clausilia bidentata   Two-Toothed Door Snail
Cochlicopa lubrica   Slippery Moss Snail
Deroceras reticulatum   Netted Slug
Discus rotundatus   Rounded Snail
Ferrisia wautieri   a freshwater limpet
Gyraulus albus   White Ram's Horn

Gyraulis crista	Nautilus Ram's Horn
Gyraulis laevis	Smooth/Small Ram's Horn
Helix aspersa	Garden Snail
Hippeutis complanatus	Flat Ramshorn
Hydrobia ulvae	Laver Spire Snail
Hydrobia ventrosa agg.	Spire Snail
Lauria cylindracea	Common Chrysalis Snail
Lymnaea peregra	Wandering Snail
Lymnaea stagnalis	Great Pond Snail
Lymnaea truncatula	Dwarf Pond Snail
Monacha cantiana	Kentish Snail
Musculium lacustre	Orb Mussel
Nesovitrea hammonis	
Ovatella myosotis	Mouse-eared Snail
Oxychilus alliarius	Garlic Snail
Oxychilus cellarius	Cellar Snail
Oxychilus helveticus	Glossy Glass Snail
Paludinella littorina	Lagoon Snail
Pisidium nitidum	Pea Shell
Pisidium obtusale	Pea Shell
Pisidium personatum	Pea Shell
Pisidium subtruncatum	Pea Shell
Physia acuta	
Potamopyrgus antipodarum	Jenkins' Spire Snail
Trichia hispida	Hairy Snail
Vallonia costata	Ribbed Grass Snail
Valvata piscinalis	Common Valve Snail
Ventrosa ventrosa	
Vitrea contracta	Milky Crystal Snail

ANNELIDS

HIRUNDINEA	**LEECHES**
Erpobdella octoculata	
Erpobdella testacea	
Helobdella stagnalis	
Theromyson tessulatum	

CRUSTACEA

Argulus foliaceus	Fish Louse
Asellus aquaticus	
Asellus meridianus	
Crangonyx pseudogracilis	Freshwater Shrimp
Daphnia agg.	Water Flea
Gammarus pulex	Freshwater Shrimp
Gammarus duebeni	Brackish Water Shrimp
Gammarus zaddachi	Brackish Water Shrimp
Lekanspherae rugicauda	
Palaemonetes varians	
Sphaeroma rugicauda	

ARACHNIDA

ACARI	**MITES**
Aceria macrochelus	
Aceria macrorhynchus	
Aceria varius	
Aculus tetanothrix	
Eriophyes convolvens	
Eriophyes crataegi	
Eriophyes goniothorax	
Eriophyes prunispinosae	
Eriophyes similes	
PSEUDO-SCORPIONIDA	**PSEUDOSCORPIONS**
Chthonius ischnocheles	
Neobisium carcinioides	
OPILIONES	**HARVESTMEN**
Anelasmocephalus cambridgei	
Homalenotus quadridentatus	
Lacinius ephippiatus	
Leiobunum blackwalli	
Leiobunum rotundum	
Lophopilio palpinalis	
Mitopus morio	
Mitostoma chrysomelas	
Nemastoma bimaculatum	
Oligolophus hanseni	
Oligolophus tridens	
Opilio parietinus	
Opilio saxatilis	
Paroligolophus agrestis	
Paroligolophus meadii	
Phalangium opilio	
Rilaena triangularis	
ARANEAE	**SPIDERS**

Agelena labyrinthica   Field Sheet Web Spider
Agroeca brunnea
Agroeca inopina
Alopecosa barbipes
Amaurobius fenestralis
Amaurobius similis
Anelosimus vittatus
Araneus diadematus   Garden Spider
Araniella cucurbitina
Bathyphantes gracilis
Bathyphantes parvulus
Centromerita concinna
Centromerus dilutus
Centromerus sylvaticus
Clubiona comta
Clubiona reclusa
Clubiona stagnatilis
Crustulina guttata
Dictyna arundinacea
Dictyna uncinata
Dicymbium brevisitosum
Drassodes cupreus
Enoplognatha mordax
Enoplognatha ovata
Episinus angulatus
Erigone atra
Erigone dentipalpis
Ero cambridgei
Ero furcata
Gibbaranea gibbosa
Gnathonarium dentatum
Gonatium rubens
Gongylidium rufipes
Hahnia nava
Harpactea hombergi
Heliophanus flavipes
Hylyphantes graminicola
Kaestneria dorsalis
Kaestneria pullata
Larinioides cornutus
Lepthyphantes alacris
Lepthyphantes ericaeus
Lepthyphantes flavipes
Lepthyphantes mengei

Lepthyphantes pallidus
Lepthyphantes tenuis
Lepthyphantes zimmermanni
Linyphia hortensis
Linyphia triangularis
Macrargus rufus
Metellina mengei
Metellina segmentata
Micaria pulicaria
Micrargus herbigradus
Microlinyphia pusilla
Microneta viaria
Monocephalus fuscipes
Nereine clathrata
Nereine montana
Nigma puella
Nuctenea umbratica
Oedothorax gibbosus
Pachygnatha clercki
Pachygnatha degeeri
Pardosa amentata
Pardosa monticola
Pardosa nigriceps
Pardosa prativaga
Pardosa pullata
Pardosa purbeckensis
Peponocranium ludicrum
Philodromus aureolus
Philodromus cespitum
Pholcus phalangioides   Daddylonglegs Spider
Phrurolithus festivus
Pisaura mirabilis   Nursery Web Spider
Pocadicnemis juncea
Porrhomma pygmaeum
Robertus lividus
Salticus scenicus   Zebra Spider
Silometopus ambiguus
Steatoda bipunctata
Tetragnatha extensa
Tetragnatha montana
Tetragnatha nigrita
Tetragnatha pinicola
Theridion sisyphium

Theridion varians
Trochosa ruricola
Trochosa terricola
Troxochrus scabriculus
Typhochrestus digitatus
Walckenaeria acuminata
Walckenaeria antica
Walckenaeria nudipalpis
Walckenaeria unicornis
Xysticus erraticus
Xysticus kochi
Zilla diodia
Zora spinimana
Zygiella atrica
Zygiella x-notata

EPHEMEN-OPTERA

MAYFLIES

Caenis robusta
Cloeon dipterum

ODONATA

DRAGONFLIES & DAMSELFLIES

Aeshna cyanea	Southern Hawker
Aeshna grandis	Brown Hawker
Aeshna mixta	Migrant Hawker
Anax imperator	Emperor Dragonfly
Brachytron pratense	Hairy Dragonfly
Calopteryx splendens	Banded Demoiselle
Coenagrion puella	Azure Damselfly
Enallagma cyathigerum	Common Blue Damselfly
Erythromma viridulum	Small Red-eyed Damselfly
Ischnura elegans	Blue-Tailed Damselfly
Lestes dryas	Scarce Emerald Damselfly
Lestes sponsa	Emerald Damselfly
Libellula depressa	Broad-Bodied Chaser
Libellula quadrimaculata	Four-Spotted Chaser
Orthetrum cancellatum	Black-Tailed Skimmer
Pyrrhosoma nymphula	Large Red Damselfly
Sympetrum flaveolum	Yellow-Winged Darter
Sympetrum sanguineum	Ruddy Darter
Sympetrum striolatum	Common Darter

ORTHOPTERA

GRASSHOPPERS & CRICKETS

Chorthippus albomarginatus	Lesser Marsh Grasshopper
Chorthippus brunneus	Common Field Grasshopper
Chorthippus parallelus	Meadow Grasshopper
Conocephalus dorsalis	Short-Winged Conehead
Leptophyes punctatissima	Speckled Bush Cricket
Meconema thalassinum	Oak Bush Cricket
Metrioptera roeselii	Roesel's Bush Cricket
Pholidoptera griseoaptera	Dark Bush Cricket
Tetrix subulata	Slender Ground Hopper

HEMIPTERA

LAND & WATER BUGS

HETEROPTERA

TRUE BUGS

Alydus calcaratus	
Callicorixa praeusta	
Ceraleptus lividus	
Corixa affinis	
Corixa panzeri	
Corixa punctata	Punctate Corixa
Cymatia coleoptrata	
Deraeocoris ruber	
Drymus brunneus	
Gerris gibbifer	
Gerris lacustris	Common Pondskater
Gerris odontogaster	Toothed Pondskater
Gerris thoracicus	
Hesperocorixa linnaei	
Hesperocorixa sahlbergi	
Hesperocorixa moesta	
Hydrometra stagnorum	Water Measurer
Ilyocoris cimicoides	
Leptopterna dolabrata	
Lygocoris pabulinus	Common Green Capsid
Lygus maritimus	
Mesovelia furcata	
Micronecta scholtzi	
Microvelia pygmea	
Microvelia reticulata	
Nepa cinerea	Water Scorpion
Notonecta glauca	Backswimmer

Notonecta viridis	Backswimmer	Alianta incana	
Notostira elongata		Altica lythri	
Orthotylus marginalis	Dark Green Apple Capsid	Altica palustris	
Plagiognathus arbustorum		Amara aenea	Common Sun Beetle
Picromerus bidens		Amara apricaria	
Plea leachi		Amara bifrons	
Ranatra linearis	Water Stick Insect	Amara (Curtonotus) convexiuscula	
Salda littoralis		Amara ovata	
Sigara distincta		Amara similata	
Sigara dorsalis		Amara tibialis	
Sigara falleni		Amischa analis	
Sigara fossarum		Anacaena bipustulata	
Sigara lateralis		Anacaena globulus	
Sigara nigrolineata		Anacaena limbata	
Sigara concinna		Anacaena lutescens	
Sigara limitata		Anaspis costai	
Sigara stagnalis		Anaspis garneysi	
Sigara selecta		Anaspis pulicaria	
Syromastes rhombeus		Anatis ocellata	Eyed Ladybird

HOMOPTERA

		Anisosticta novemdecimpunctata	19-Spot Ladybird
Cercopis vulnerata	Red & Black Froghopper	Anoplodera (Pseudoalosterna) livida	
Schizoneura lanuginosa	Elm Pouch Gall	Anotylus rugosus	

COLEOPTERA   **BEETLES**

		Anotylus sculpturatus	
Acalles misellus		Anthicus antherinus	
Achenium depressum		Anthicus constrictus	
Acilius sulcatus		Anthonomus pedicularius	
Acrotona (Atheta) muscorum		Anthrenus verbasci	Museum Beetle
Acupalpus dubius		Aphodius ater	
Acupalpus meridianus		Apion (Perapion) curtirostre	
Adalia bipunctata	Two-Spot Ladybird	Apion (Protapion) fulvipes	White Clover Seed Weevil
Adonia (Hippodamia) variegata	Adonis' Ladybird	Apion (Pirapion) immune	
Agabus bipustulatus		Apion (Ischnopterapion) io	
Agabus conspersus		Apion (Pseudaplemonus) limonii	
Agabus guttatus		Apion (Malvapion) malvae	
Agabus nebulosus			
Agabus sturmii		Apion (Protapion) nigritarse	
Agonum fuliginosum		Apion onopordi	
Agonum marginatum		Apion (Aspidapion) radiolus	
Agriotes sputator			
Aleochara (algarum) obscurella			

Apion (Protapion) trifolii	Clover Seed Weevil
Apion (Exapion) ulicis	Gorse Weevil
Aridius bifasciatus	
Astenus lyonessius	
Athous haemorrhoidalis	
Attagenus pellio	Two-Spotted Carpet Beetle
Autalia impressa	
Bembidion articulatum	
Bembidion femoratum	
Bembidion iricolor	
Bembidion minimum	
Bembidion varium	
Berosus affinis	
Berosus signaticollis	
Brachygluta fossulata	
Brachygluta helferi	
Brachypterus glaber	
Brachypterus urticae	Nettle Pollen Beetle
Bradycellus harpalinus	
Bruchus loti	
Brundinia meridionalis	
Byrrhus pilula	Pill Beetle
Byturus tomentosus	Raspberry Beetle
Cafius xantholoma	
Calathus fuscipes	
Cantharis decipiens	
Cantharis pallida	
Cantharis rufa var. darwiniana	
Cantharis rustica	
Cassida rubiginosa	Thistle Tortoise Beetle
Cassida vittata	Bordered Tortoise Beetle
Catops grandicollis	
Cercyon convexiusculus	
Cercyon haemorrhoidalis	
Cercyon littoralis	
Cercyon sternalis	
Cercyon unipunctatus	
Ceutorhynchus asperifoliarum	
Ceutorhynchus assimilis	Cabbage Seed Weevil
Ceutorhynchus pollinarius	
Ceutorhynchus rapae	

Ceutorhynchus rugulosus	
Chaetocnema concinna	Beet Flea Beetle
Chrysolina banksi	
Chrysolina polita	Knotgrass Leaf Beetle
Cicindela campestris	Green Tiger Beetle
Clytus arietis	Wasp Beetle
Coccinella septempunctata	Seven-Spot Ladybird
Coccinella undecimpunctata	11-Spot Ladybird
Coelostoma orbiculare	
Copelatus haemorrhoidalis	
Colymbetes fuscus	
Corticaria impressa	
Corticaria punctulata	
Cortinicara gibbosa	
Crepidodera (Chalcoides) aurata	Willow Flea Beetle
Crepidodera (Chalcoides) aurea	
Crepidodera (Chalcoides) fulvicornis	
Curculio glandium	Acorn Weevil
Cymbiodyta marginella	
Cypha longicornis	
Demetrias atricapillus	
Dicheirotrichus gustavi	
Dolichosoma lineare	
Dorcus parallelipipedus	Lesser Stag Beetle
Dorytomus taeniatus	
Dromius linearis	
Dromius melanocephalus	
Dromius meridionalis	
Dromius notatus	
Dromius quadrimaculatus	
Dromius quadrinotatus	
Drusilla canaliculata	
Dryops luridus	
Dyschirius luedersi	
Dytiscus marginalis	Great Diving Beetle
Dytiscus semisulcatus	
Elaphrus cupreus	
Elaphrus riparius	
Endomychus coccineus	
Enochrus coarctatus	

Enochrus halophilus

Enochrus melanocephalus

Enochrus testaceus

Epuraea deleta

Epuraea (florea) pallescens

Erichsonius cinerascens

Exochomus quadripustulatus   Pine Ladybird

Galerucella pusilla

Geotrupes stercorarius   Dor Beetle

Grammoptera abdominalis   *(=variegata)*

Graptodytes bilineatus

Gronops lunatus

Gymnetron rostellum

Gyrinus substriatus

Haliplus immaculatus

Haliplus laminatus

Haliplus lineatocollis

Haliplus ruficollis

Halyzia sedecimguttata   Orange Ladybird

Harpalus affinis

Harpalus attenuatus

Harpalus rubripes

Harpalus rufipes   Strawberry Seed Beetle

Harpalus smaragdinus

Helochares lividus

Helochares punctatus

Helophorus aequalis

Helophorus brevipalpis

Helophorus minutus

Helophorus obscurus

Helops caeruleus

Heterocerus fenestratus

Heterocerus obsoletus

Hydraena testacea

Hydrobius fuscipes

Hydrochus angustatus

Hydroglyphus (pusillus) geminus

Hydrophilus piceus   Great Silver Water Beetle

Hygrobia hermanni   Screech Beetle

Hydroporus angustatus

Hygroporus discretus

Hygroporus erythrocephalus

Hygroporus gyllenhalli

Hygroporus memnonius

Hygroporus palustris

Hydroporus planus

Hydroporus pubescens

Hydroporus tessellatus

Hygrotus impressopunctotus   *(=Coelambus)*

Hygrotus inaequalis

Hygrotus parallelogrammus   *(=Coelambus)*

Hylastinus obscurus   Gorse Bark Beetle

Hyphydrus ovatus

Ilybius ater

Ilybius (Agabus) chalconatus

Ilybius fuliginosus

Ilybius (Agabus) montanus   *(= melanocornis)*

Ilybius quadriguttatus

Ischnosoma splendidum   *(=Mycetoporus)*

Kibunea minuta

Laccobius minutus

Laccophilus hyalinus

Lagria hirta

Lathrobium terminatum

Limnoxenus niger

Leistus ferrugineus

Litargus connexus

Lochmaea crataegi   Hawthorn Leaf Beetle

Longitarsus dorsalis

Lucanus cervus   Stag Beetle

Magdalis cerasi

Malachius bipustulatus   Malachite Beetle

Malthinus flaveolus

Malthinus seriepunctatus

Malthodes minimus

Mecinus collaris

Megasternum (obscurum) concinnum

Meligethes aeneus   Common Pollen Beetle

Meligethes viridescens

Pheronome lures in muslin bags attract day-flying clearwing moths.

Meloe proscarabaeus	Oil Beetle
Melolontha melolontha	Common Cockchafer
Microlestes maurus	
Microlestes minutulus	
Mycetophagus multipunctatus	
Myllaena intermedia	
Nebria brevicollis	
Necrodes littoralis	Shore Sexton Beetle
Nedynus quadrimaculatus	Small Nettle Weevil
Neocrepidodera transversa	(formerly Crepidodera)
Nicrophorus humator	Black Sexton Beetle
Notaris scirpi	
Noterus clavicornis	Larger Noterus
Notiophilus biguttatus	
Notiophilus palustris	

Notiophilus quadripunctatus	
Ochthebius minimus	
Ochthebius viridis	
Ocypus brunnipes	
Oedemera lurida	
Oedemera nobilis	Swollen-thigh Beetle
Olibrus aeneus	
Olisthopus rotundatus	
Omonodus (Anthicus) floralis	
Otiorhynchus singularis	Raspberry Weevil
Otiorhynchus sulcatus	Vine Weevil
Oulema melanopus	Cereal Leaf Beetle
Oxypoda elongatula	
Panagaeus bipustulatus	
Peltodytes caesus	
Phaedon armoraciae	Mustard Beetle

Phaedon cochleariae	Mustard Beetle	Rutpela (Leptura)maculata	
Philonthus fumarius		Rybaxis (laminata) longicornis	
Philonthus succicola			
Phloeotribus rhododactylus		Scaphidium quadrimaculatum	
Phyllobius argentatus	Silver-Green Leaf Weevil	Sciodrepoides watsoni	
Phyllobius pomaceus		Scymnus frontalis	
Phyllobius roboretanus	Small Green Nettle Weevil	Sepedophilus nigripennis	
Phyllobius viridiaeris	Green Nettle Weevil	Sermylassa halensis	
Phyllotreta nemorum	Turnip Flea Beetle	Simplocaria semistriata	
Platynus (Agonum) obscurum		Sitona lineatus	Pea And Bean Weevil
Podagrica fuscicornis	Mallow Flea Beetle	Sitona regensteinensis	
Pogonus chalceus		Soronia grisea	
Polydrusus cervinus		Sphaeroderma rubidum	
Polydrusus (undatus) tereticollis		Sphaeroderma testaceum	
Propylea quattuordecimpunctata	14-Spot Ladybird	Stenagostus rhombeus	
Proteinus ovalis		Stenolophus mixtus	
Pseudotriphyllus suturalis		Stenus latifrons	
Psyllobora vigintiduopunctata	22-Spot Ladybird	Stenus providus	
Pterostichus diligens		Stephostethus lardarius	
Pterostichus melanarius		Stilbus testaceus	
Pterostichus minor		Subcoccinella vigintiquattuorpunctata	24-Spot Ladybird
Pterostichus nigrita agg.		Suphrodytes dorsalis	
Ptomaphagus subvillosus		Syntomus (Metabletus) foveatus	
Pyrochroa coccinea	Black-Headed Cardinal Beetle	Tachinus signatus	
Pyrochroa serraticornis	Common Cardinal Beetle	Tachyporus chrysomelinus	
Quedius (pallipes) simplicifrons		Tachyporus hypnorum	
Rhagonycha lignosa		Tachyporus tersus	
Rhagonycha limbata		Tasgius (Ocypus) ater	
Rhantus frontalis		Telmatophilus typhae	
Rhinosimus planirostris		Thanasimus formicarius	Ant Beetle
Rhizophagus bipustulatus		Thinobaena (Atheta) vestita	
Rhynchaenus alni		Trachyphloeus angustisetulus	
Rhynchaenus rusci		Trichocellus placidus	
Rhynchites aequatus	Apple Fruit Rhynchites	Typhaeus typhoeus	Minotaur Beetle
Rhynchites caeruleus	Apple Twig Cutter	Tytthaspis sedecimpunctata	16-Spot Ladybird
Rhynchites germanicus	Strawberry Rhynchites	Xantholinus longiventris	

MEGALOPTERA ALDERFLIES

Sialis lutaria

MECOPTERA SCORPION FLIES

Panorpa communis

HYMENOPTERA SAWFLIES, BEES, WASPS & ANTS

Species marked* have not been recorded since 1980, or are of suspect determination.

Agenioideus cinctellus	
Aglaostigma aucupariae	
Aglaostigma fulvipes	
Ammophila sabulosa	Red Banded Sand Wasp
Ancistrocerus gazella	
*Ancistrocerus parietinus**	
Ancistrocerus parietinum	Wall Mason Wasp
*Ancistrocerus trifasciatus**	
Andrena bicolor	Gwynne's Mining Bee
Andrena bimaculata	
Andrena clarkella	
Andrena denticulata	
Andrena dorsata	
Andrena flavipes	Yellow Legged Mining Bee
Andrena fucata	
Andrena labialis	
Andrena labiata	Girdling Mining Bee
Andrena minutula	
Andrena nigroaenea	
*Adrena ovatula**	
Andrena praecox	
Andrena scotica	
Andrena subopaca	
Andrena trimmerana	Trimmer's Mining Bee
Andrena wilkella	
Andricus fecundator	
Andricus kollari	
Andricus lignicola	
Andricus quercuscalicis	Knopper Gall causer
Anthophora bimaculata	
Anthophora plumipes	Hairy Footed Flower Bee

Apis mellifera	Honeybee
Arachnospila anceps	
Arachnospila spissa	
*Arachnospila trivialis**	
Arge ustulata	
Astata boops	
Athalia cordata	
Biorhiza pallida f. sexual	Oak Apple Gall causer
Blennocampa (phyllocolpa) pusilla	
Bombus campestris	
Bombus lapidarius	Large Red Tailed Bumble Bee
Bombus lucorum	White-Tailed Bumble Bee
Bombus pascuorum	Common Carder Bee
Bombus pratorum	Early Bumble Bee
Bombus (Psithyrus) sylvestris	Four Coloured Cuckoo Bee
Bombus terrestris	Buff-Tailed Bumble Bee
Bombus (Psithyrus) vestalis	Vestal Cuckoo Bee
Caliadurgus fasciatellus	
Cephus cultratus	
Cerceris arenaria	Sand Tailed Digger Wasp
Cerceris quinquefasciata	5-Banded Tailed Digger Wasp
Cerceris rybyensis	Ornate Tailed Digger Wasp
Chrysis ignita	
Chrysura radians	
Colletes fodiens	
Colletes halophilus	
*Colletes succinctus**	
Crabro cribrarius	Slender Bodied Digger Wasp
Crossocerus annulipes	
Crossocerus podagricus	
Cynips quercusfolii f. agamic	Cherry Gall causer
Crossocerus quadrimaculatus	4-Spotted Digger Wasp
Dinotoides tenebricus	
Diodontus luperus	
Diodontus minutus	Minute Black Wasp
Diodontus tristis	Melancholy Black Wasp
Diplolepis eglanteriae	

Diplolepis nervosa	
Diplolepis rosae	Robin's Pin-Cushion Gall causer
Dolichovespula sylvestris	Tree Wasp
Ectemnius cavifrons*	
Ectemnius continuus	
Ectemnius lituratus	
Ectemnius rubicola*	
Epeolus variegatus	
Episyron rufipes	Red Legged Spider Wasp
Eupotania (Pontania) pedunculi	
Evagetes crassicornis	
Hedychridium roseum	
Hedychrum niemalai	
Hoplitis claviventris	
Hylaeus brevicornis	Short Horned Yellow-Face Bee
Hylaeus communis	Common Yellow Face Bee
Hylaeus signatus	Large Yellow-Faced Bee
Lasioglossum albipes	
Lasioglossum calceatum	Slender Mining Bee
Lasioglossum leucopus	
Lasioglossum leucozonium	
Lasioglossum malachurum	
Lasioglossum minutissimum	Least Mining Bee
Lasioglossum morio	Brassy Mining Bee
Lasioglossum nitidiusculum*	Neat Mining Bee
Lasioglossum parvulum	
Lasioglossum pauxillum	
Lasioglossum puncticolle	
Lasioglossum smeathmanellum	
Lasioglossum villosulum	Shaggy Mining Bee
Lasius flavus	Yellow Meadow Ant
Lasius fuliginosus	Jet Ant
Lasius niger	Small Black Ant
Leptothorax acervorum	Slender Ant
Lindenius albilabris	
Liposthenus latreillei	
Macrophya albicincta	

Macrophya ribis	
Megachile dorsalis	Silvery Leaf-Cutter Bee
Megachile maritima	Coastal Leaf-Cutter Bee
Megachile willughbiella	
Melecta albifrons	
Mellinus arvensis	Field Digger Wasp
Messa nana	
Mimesa equestris*	
Mutilla europaea	Large Velvet Ant
Myrmica rubra	Red Ant
Myrmica ruginodis	Red Ant
Myrmica scabrinodis	Red Ant
Myrmica schencki	Red Ant
Myrmosa atra	Black Headed Velvet Ant
Neuroterus albipes f. agamic	Smooth Spangle Gall causer
Neuroterus numismalis f. agamic	Silk-Button Spangle Gall causer
Neuroterus quercusbaccarum f.agamic	Common Spangle Gall causer
Nomada fabriciana	Fabricius' Nomad Bee
Nomada flava	
Nomada flavoguttata	
Nomada fucata	
Nomada goodeniana	Gooden's Nomad Bee
Nomada marshamella	Marsham's Nomad Bee
Nomada ruficornis	Red-Horned Nomad Bee
Nomada rufipes*	Golden-Rod Nomad Bee
Nomada striata	
Nysson trimaculatus	
Odynerus spinipes	Spiny Mason Wasp
Osmia rufa	Red Mason Bee
Oxybelus uniglumis	Common Spiny Digger Wasp
Passaloecus gracilis	
Passaloecus singularis	
Philanthus triangulum	Bee Wolf
Pompilus cinereus*	Leaden Spider Wasp
Pontania bridgmani	
Poodolerus (Dolerus) niger	
Pontania proxima	
Profenusa pygmaea	
Smicromyrme rufipes	Small Velvet Ant

Sphecodes crassus
Sphecodes ephippius
Sphecodes geoffrellus
Sphecodes miniatus*
Sphecodes monilicornis
Sphecodes pellucidus
Sphecodes rubicundus
Tachysphex pompiliformis
Trichrysis cyanea
Trypoxylon attenuatum — Slender Wood Borer Wasp
Trypoxylon figulus
Vespa crabro — Hornet
Vespula germanica — German Wasp
Vespula vulgaris — Common Wasp

LEPIDOPTERA — MOTHS & BUTTERFLIES

MOTHS

Abraxas grossulariata — Magpie
Abraxas sylvata — Clouded Magpie
Abrostola tripartita — Spectacle
Acentria ephemerella — Water Veneer
Achlya flavicornis — Yellow Horned
Acleris bergmanniana
Acleris cristana
Acleris emargana
Acleris ferrugana
Acleris holmiana
Acleris kochiella
Acleris laterana
Acleris rhombana — Rhomboid Tortrix
Acleris variegana — Garden Rose Tortrix
Acrobasis consociella
Acrolepia autumnitella Curtis
Acronicta aceris — Sycamore
Acronicta leporina — Miller
Acronicta megacephala — Poplar Grey
Acronicta psi — Grey Dagger
Acronicta rumicis — Knot Grass
Acronicta tridens — Dark Dagger
Adela reaumurella
Adela rufimitrella

Aethalura punctulata — Grey Birch
Aethes cnicana
Aethes rubigana
Aethes tesserana
Agapeta hamana
Agdistis bennetii — Sea-lavender Plume
Agonopterix alstromeriana
Agonopterix arenella
Agonopterix assimilella
Agonopterix heracliana
Agonopterix nervosa
Agonopterix ocellana
Agonopterix umbellana
Agriopis leucophaearia — Spring Usher
Agriopis marginaria — Dotted Border
Agriphila geniculea
Agriphila inquinatella
Agriphila latistria
Agriphila selasella
Agriphila straminella
Agriphila tristella
Agrochola circellaris — Brick
Agrochola helvola — Flounced Chestnut
Agrochola litura — Brown-spot Pinion
Agrochola lota — Red-line Quaker
Agrochola lychnidis — Beaded Chestnut
Agrochola macilenta — Yellow-line Quaker
Agrotis exclamationis — Heart and Dart
Agrotis ipsilon — Dark Sword-grass
Agrotis puta — Shuttle-shaped Dart
Agrotis segetum — Turnip Moth
Agrotis vestigialis — Archer's Dart
Alabonia geoffrella
Alcis repandata — Mottled Beauty
Aleimma loeflingiana
Aleucis distinctata — Sloe Carpet
Allophyes oxyacanthae — Green-brindled Crescent
Alsophila aescularia — March Moth
Alucita hexadactyla — Twenty-plume Moth
Amphipoea oculea — Ear Moth
Amphipyra berbera svenssoni — Svensson's Copper Underwing
Amphipyra pyramidea — Copper Underwing

Amphipyra tragopoginis	Mouse Moth
Anacampsis populella	
Anarsia spartiella	
Ancylis achatana	
Ancylis badiana	
Ancylosis oblitella	
Anthophila fabriciana	
Anticlea badiata	Shoulder Stripe
Anticlea derivata	Streamer
Apamea anceps	Large Nutmeg
Apamea crenata	Clouded-bordered Brindle
Apamea lithoxylaea	Light Arches
Apamea monoglypha	Dark Arches
Apamea oblonga	Crescent Striped
Apamea ophiogramma	Double Lobed
Apamea remissa	Dusky Brocade
Apamea scolopacina	Slender Brindle
Apamea sordens	Rustic Shoulder-knot
Apamea unanimis	Small Clouded Brindle
Aphelia paleana	Timothy Tortrix
Aphomia sociella	Bee Moth
Apocheima pilosaria	Pale Brindled Beauty
Apodia bifractella	
Aporophyla lutulenta	Deep-brown Dart
Aporophyla nigra	Black Rustic
Apotomis betuletana	
Apotomis capreana	
Apotomis turbidana	
Archanara geminipuncta	Twin-spotted Wainscot
Archiearis parthenias	Orange Underwing
Archips podana	Large Fruit-tree Tortrix
Archips rosana	Rose Tortrix
Arctia caja	Garden Tiger
Arctia villica britannica	Cream-spot Tiger
Arenostola phragmitidis	Fen Wainscot
Argyresthia bonnetella	
Argyresthia brockeella	
Argyresthia curvella	
Argyresthia goedartella	
Argyresthia laevigatella	
Argyresthia pygmaeella	
Argyresthia retinella	
Argyresthia semifusca	

Aristotelia brizella	
Atethmia centrago	Centre-barred Sallow
Autographa gamma	Silver Y
Autographa jota	Plain Golden Y
Autographa pulchrina	Beautiful Golden Y
Axylia putris	Flame
Bactra lancealana	
Bactra robustana	
Batia lunaris	
Batia unitella	
Batrachedra praeangusta	
Bembecia ichneumoniformis	Six-belted Clearwing
Bena bicolorana	Scarce Silver-lines
Biston betularia	Peppered Moth
Biston strataria	Oak Beauty
Blastobasis decolorella	
Blastodacna hellerella	
Bohemannia pulverosella	
Borkhausenia fuscescens	
Brachionycha sphinx	Sprawler
Brachmia blandella	
Brachylomia viminalis	Minor Shoulder-knot
Bryotropha affinis	
Bryotropha desertella	
Bryotropha terrella	
Bucculatrix albedinella	
Bucculatrix bechsteinella	
Bucculatrix demaryella	
Bucculatrix maritima	
Bucculatrix ulmella	
Cabera exanthemata	Common Wave
Cabera pusaria	Common White Wave
Cacoecimorpha pronubana	Carnation Tortrix
Calamotropha paludella	
Callistege mi	Mother Shipton
Calliteara pudibunda	Pale Tussock
Caloptilia betulicola	
Caloptilia elongella	
Caloptilia robustella	
Caloptilia stigmatella	
Caloptilia syringella	
Campaea margaritata	Light Emerald

Camptogramma bilineata — Yellow Shell
Caradrina morpheus — Mottled Rustic
Carcina quercana
Carpatolechia proximella
Cataclysta lemnata — Small China-mark
Catocala nupta — Red Underwing
Catoptria falsella
Catoptria pinella
Cedestis gysseleniella
Cedestis subfasciella
Celaena leucostigma — Crescent
Celypha cespitana
Celypha lacunana
Celypha striana
Cerapteryx graminis — Antler Moth
Cerastis rubricosa — Red Chestnut
Cerura vinula — Puss Moth
Charanycha trigrammica — Treble Lines
Chesias legatella — Streak
Chesias rufata rufata — Broom-tip
Chiasma clathrata — Latticed Heath
Chilo phragmitella
Chilodes maritimus — Silky Wainscot
Chionodes fumatella
Chloroclysta truncata — Common Marbled Carpet
Chloroclystis v-ata — V-Pug
Chrysoteuchia culmella — Garden Grass-veneer
Cidaria fulvata — Barred Yellow
Cilix glaucata — Chinese Character
Clavigesta purdeyi — Pine Leaf-mining Moth
Clepsis consimilana
Clepsis spectrana — Cyclamen Tortrix
Clostera curtula — Chocolate-tip
Cnaemidophorus rhododactyla — Rose Plume
Cnephasia asseclana — Flax Tortrix
Cnephasia incertana — Light Grey Tortrix
Cnephasia stephensiana — Grey Tortrix
Cochylis atricapitana
Cochylis dubitana
Cochylis hybridella
Coenobia rufa — Small Rufous
Coleophora adjunctella
Coleophora adspersella

Coleophora albicosta
Coleophora alcyonipennella — Small Clover Case-bearer
Coleophora alticolella
Coleophora anatipennella — Pistol Case-bearer
Coleophora argentula
Coleophora artemisiella
Coleophora atriplicis
Coleophora badiipennella
Coleophora betulella
Coleophora deviella
Coleophora discordella
Coleophora flavipennella
Coleophora fuscicornis
Coleophora glaucicolella
Coleophora gryphipennella
Coleophora ibipennella
Coleophora laricella — Larch Case-bearer
Coleophora limosipennella
Coleophora lineolea
Coleophora lusciniaepennella
Coleophora lutipennella
Coleophora mayrella
Coleophora milvipennis
Coleophora otidipennella
Coleophora salicorniae
Coleophora salinella
Coleophora serratella
Coleophora siccifolia
Coleophora solitariella
Coleophora spinella
Colostygia pectinataria — Green Carpet
Colotois pennaria — Feathered Thorn
Comibaena bajularia — Blotched Emerald
Conistra vaccinii — Chestnut
Cosmia affinis — Lesser-spotted Pinion
Cosmia diffinis — White-spotted Pinion
Cosmia pyralina — Lunar-spotted Pinion
Cosmia trapezina — Dun-bar
Cosmopterix lienigiella

Cosmorhoe ocellata	Purple Bar
Crambus lathoniellus	
Crambus pascuella	
Crambus perlella	
Crocallis elinguaria	Scalloped Oak
Cryphia domestica	Marbled Beauty
Cucullia asteris	Star-wort
Cucullia chamomillae	Chamomile Shark
Cucullia umbratica	Shark
Cyclophora albipunctata	Birch Mocha
Cydia nigricana	Pea Moth
Cydia pomonella	Codling Moth
Cydia splendana	
Cydia succedana	
Deilephila elpenor	Elephant Hawk-moth
Deltaornix torquillella	
Depressaria badiella	
Depressaria sordidatella	
Diachrysia chrysitis	Burnished Brass
Diarsia brunnea	Purple Clay
Diarsia mendica	Ingrailed Clay
Diarsia rubi	Small Square-spot
Dichonia aprilina	Merveille du Jour
Dichrorampha gueneeana	
Dichrorampha petiverella	
Dichrorampha plumbana	
Diloba caeruleocephala	Figure of Eight
Dioryctria abietella	
Dioryctria simpliciella	
Dipleurina lacustrata	
Diplodoma herminata	
Discestra trifolii	Nutmeg
Ditula angustiorana	Red-barred Tortrix
Diurnea fagella	
Drepana falcataria	Pebble Hook-tip
Drymonia ruficornis	Lunar Marbled Brown
Dryobotodes eremita	Brindled Green
Dypterygia scabriuscula	Bird's Wing
Earias clorana	Cream-bordered Green Pea
Ebulea crocealis	
Ecliptopera silaceata	Small Phoenix
Ecoedemia erythrogenella	

Ectoedemia albifasciella	
Ectoedemia angulifasciella	
Ectoedemia argyropeza	
Ectoedemia atricollis	
Ectoedemia heringi	
Ectoedemia occultella	
Ectoedemia spinosella	
Ectoedemia subbimaculella	
Ectropis bistortata	Engrailed
Ectropis crepuscularia	Small Engrailed
Eilema complana	Scarce Footman
Eilema griseola	Dingy Footman
Eilema lurideola	Common Footman
Elachista argentella	
Elachista atricomella	
Elachista poae	
Elachista rufocinerea	
Electrophaes corylata	Broken-barred Carpet
Emmelina monodactyla	Common Plume
Emmetia marginea	
Endotricha flammealis	
Endrosis sarcitrella	White-shouldered House Moth
Ennomos alniaria	Canary-shouldered Thorn
Ennomos erosaria	September Thorn
Epagoge grotiana	
Epiblema cynosbatella	
Epiblema trimaculana	
Epiblema uddmanniana	Bramble Shoot Moth
Epichnopterix plumella	
Epichnopterix retiella	
Epinotia abbreviana	
Epinotia bilunana	
Epinotia cruciana	
Epinotia nisella	
Epinotia subocellana	
Epinotia trigonella	
Epione repandaria	Bordered Beauty
Epirrhoe alternata	Common Carpet
Epirrita dilutata	November Moth
Eremobia ochroleuca	Dusky Sallow

Eriocrania sparrmannella	
Eriocrania subpurpurella	
Esperia sulphurella	
Ethmia terminella	
Eucosma campoliliana	
Eucosma cana	
Eucosma catoptrana	
Eucosma hohenwartiana	
Eucosma tripoliana	
Eudemis profundana	
Eudonia angustea	
Eudonia mercurella	
Eugnorisma glareosa	Autumnal Rustic
Eulamprotes atrella	
Eulamprotes unicolorella	
Eulithis pyraliata	Barred Straw
Eulithis testata	Chevron
Euphyia unagulata	Sharp-angled Carpet
Eupithecia abbreviata	Brindled Pug
Eupithecia absinthiata	Wormwood Pug
Eupithecia centaureata	Lime-speck Pug
Eupithecia dodoneata	Oak-tree Pug
Eupithecia exiguata exiguata	Mottled Pug
Eupithecia icterata	Tawny-speckled Pug
Eupithecia intricata	Freyer's Pug
Eupithecia inturbata	Maple Pug

Eupithecia millefoliata	Yarrow Pug
Eupithecia pulchellata	Foxglove Pug
Eupithecia simpliciata	Plain Pug
Eupithecia subfuscata	Grey Pug
Eupithecia subumbrata	Shaded Pug
Eupithecia succenturiata	Bordered Pug
Eupithecia tenuiata	Slender Pug
Eupithecia tripunctaria	White-spotted Pug
Eupithecia vulgata	Common Pug
Euplexia lucipara	Small Angle Shades
Euproctis chrysorrhoea	Brown-tail
Euproctis similis	Yellow-tail
Eupsilia transversa	Satellite
Eurrhypara hortulata	Small Magpie
Euthrix potatoria	Drinker
Euxoa cursoria	Coast Dart
Euxoa nigricans	Garden Dart
Euxoa tritici	White-line Dart
Euzophera pinguis	
Evergestis pallidata	
Falcaria lacertinaria	Scalloped Hook-tip
Furcula furcula	Sallow Kitten
Gastropacha quercifolia	Lappet
Gelechia sororculella	
Geometra papilionaria	Large Emerald
Glyphipterix fuscoviridella	

Glyphipterix simpliciella	Cocksfoot Moth		*Idaea aversata*	Riband Wave
Goniodoma limoniella			*Idaea biselata*	Small Fan-footed Wave
Gortyna flavago	Frosted Orange		*Idaea dimidiata*	Single-dotted Wave
Graphiphora augur	Double Dart		*Idaea emarginata*	Small Scallop
Grapholita compositella			*Idaea seriata*	Small Dusty Wave
Grapholita internana			*Idaea straminata*	Plain Wave
Grapholita janthinana			*Idaea subsericeata*	Satin Wave
Grapholita jungiella			*Incurvaria masculella*	
Grapholita tenebrosana			*Lacanobia oleracea*	Bright-line Brown-eye
Gymnoscelis rufifasciata	Double-striped Pug		*Lacanobia suasa*	Dog's Tooth
Gynnidomorpha alismana			*Lacanobia thalassina*	Pale-shouldered Brocade
Gynnidomorpha vectisana			*Lacanobia w-latinum*	Light Brocade
Gypsonoma dealbana			*Lampropteryx suffumata*	Water Carpet
Habrosyne pyritoides	Buff Arches		*Laothoe populi*	Poplar Hawk-moth
Hada plebeja	Shears		*Lasiocampa quercus*	Oak Eggar
Hadena bicruris	Lychnis		*Laspeyria flexula*	Beautiful Hook-tip
Hadena rivularis	Campion		*Leucoma salicis*	White Satin Moth
Hedya nubiferana	Marbled Orchard Tortrix		*Leucoptera malifoliella*	Pear Leaf Blister Moth
Hedya ochroleucana			*Leucoptera spartifoliella*	
Hedya pruniana	Plum Tortrix		*Ligdia adustata*	Scorched Carpet
Hedya salicella			*Limnaecia phragmitella*	
Helcystogramma rufescens			*Lithophane leautieri hesperica*	Blair's Shoulder-knot
Heliozela hammoniella			*Lithophane ornitopus lactipennis*	Grey Shoulder-knot
Heliozela sericiella			*Lobesia abscisana*	
Hemiostola chrysoprasaria	Small Emerald		*Lobophora halterata*	Seraphim
Hemithea aestivaria	Common Emerald		*Lomaspilis marginata*	Clouded Border
Hepialus humuli	Ghost Moth		*Lomographa bimaculata*	White-pinion Spotted
Hepialus lupulinus	Common Swift		*Lomographa temerata*	Clouded Silver
Hepialus sylvina	Orange Swift		*Lozotaenia forsterana*	
Herminea grisealis	Small Fan-foot		*Luperina testacea*	Flounced Rustic
Hofmannophila pseudospretella	Brown House Moth		*Lycia hirtaria*	Brindled Beauty
Homoeosoma sinuella			*Lycophotia porphyrea*	True Lover's Knot
Hoplodrina alsines	Uncertain		*Lyonetia clerkella*	Apple Leaf Miner
Hoplodrina ambigua	Vine's Rustic		*Macaria liturata*	Tawny-barred Angle
Hoplodrina blanda	Rustic		*Macaria notata*	Peacock Moth
Hydraecia micacea	Rosy Rustic		*Macrochilo cribrumalis*	Dotted Fan-foot
Hydriomena furcata	July Highflier		*Macroglossum stellatarum*	Humming-bird Hawk-moth
Hyloicus pinastri	Pine Hawk-moth		*Malacosoma castrensis*	Ground Lackey
Hypena proboscidalis	Snout		*Malacosoma neustria*	Lackey
Hypsopygia costalis	Gold Triangle		*Mamestra brassicae*	Cabbage Moth
			Meganola albula	Kent Black Arches

Melanchra persicariae	Dot Moth	*Nomophila noctuella*	Rush Veneer
Melanchra pisi	Broom Moth	*Nonagria typhae*	Bulrush Wainscot
Menophra abruptaria	Waved Umber	*Notodonta dromedarius*	Iron Prominent
Mesapamea didyma	Lesser Common Rustic	*Notodonta ziczac*	Pebble Prominent
Mesapamea secalis	Common Rustic	*Nycteola revayana*	Oak Nycteoline
Mesoligia furuncula	Cloaked Minor	*Ochropacha duplaris*	Common Lutestring
Mesoligia literosa	Rosy Minor	*Ochropleura plecta*	Flame Shoulder
Micropterix aruncella		*Ocnerostoma piniariella*	
Micropterix calthella		*Odontopera bidentata*	Scalloped Hazel
Miltochrista miniata	Rosy Footman	*Oidaematophorus lithodactyla*	
Mimas tiliae	Lime Hawk-moth		
Mirificarma mulinella		*Oligia fasciuncula*	Middle-barred Minor
Mompha conturbatella		*Oligia latruncula*	Tawny Marbled Minor
Mompha epilobiella		*Oligia strigilis*	Marbled Minor
Mompha propinquella		*Oligia versicolor*	Rufous Minor
Mompha raschkiella		*Omphaloscelis lunosa*	Lunar Underwing
Mompha subbistrigella		*Opisthograptis luteolata*	Brimstone Moth
Monochroa tenebrella		*Opostega salaciella*	
Monopis laevigella	Skin Moth	*Orgyia antiqua*	Vapourer
Monopis weaverella		*Orthosia cerasi*	Common Quaker
Mythimna comma	Shoulder-striped Wainscot	*Orthosia cruda*	Small Quaker
		Orthosia gothica	Hebrew Character
Mythimna conigera	Brown-line Bright-eye	*Orthosia gracilis*	Powdered Quaker
Mythimna favicolor	Mathew's Wainscot	*Orthosia incerta*	Clouded Drab
Mythimna ferrago	Clay	*Orthosia miniosa*	Blossom Underwing
Mythimna impura	Smoky Wainscot	*Orthosia munda*	Twin-spotted Quaker
Mythimna pallens	Common Wainscot	*Orthosia opima*	Northern Drab
Mythimna pudorina	Striped Wainscot	*Orthosia populeti*	Lead-coloured Drab
Mythimna straminea	Southern Wainscot	*Orthotaenia undulana*	
Naenia typical	Gothic	*Ourapteryx sambucaria*	Swallow-tailed Moth
Nemapogon cloacella	Cork Moth	*Pammene fasciana*	
Nemophora degeerella		*Pandemis cerasana*	Barred Fruit-tree Tortrix
Neofriseria singula		*Pandemis corylana*	Chequered Fruit-tree Tortrix
Neosphaleroptera nubilana		*Pandemis heparana*	Dark Fruit-tree Tortrix
Niditinea striolella		*Panemeria tenebrata*	Small Yellow Underwing
Noctua comes	Lesser Yellow Underwing	*Panolis flammea*	Pine Beauty
Noctua fimbriata	Broad-bordered Yellow Underwing	*Paradrina clavipalpis*	Pale Mottled Willow
		Parapoynx stratiotata	Ringed China-mark
Noctua interjecta	Least Yellow Underwing	*Parastichtis suspecta*	Suspected
Noctua janthe	Lesser Broad-bordered Yellow Underwing	*Parastichtis ypsillon*	Dingy Shears
		Paraswammerdamia albicapitella	
Noctua pronuba	Large Yellow Underwing		
Nola cuculatella	Short-cloaked Moth	*Paraswammerdamia lutarea*	

Parornix anglicella
Parornix betulae
Parornix finitimella
Pasiphila chloerata   Sloe Pug
Pasiphila rectangulata   Green Pug
Pelurga comitata   Dark Spinach
Peribatodes   Willow Beauty
rhomboidaria
Peridroma saucia   Pearly Underwing
Perizoma alchemillata   Small Rivulet
Perizoma didymata   Twin-spot Carpet
Perizoma flavofasciata   Sandy Carpet
Phalera bucephala   Buff-tip

Phalonidia affinitana
Pheosia gnoma   Lesser Swallow
                                 Prominent
Pheosia tremula   Swallow Prominent
Phlogophora meticulosa   Angle Shades
Phlyctaenia coronata
Phlyctaenia perlucidalis
Phragmatobia fuliginosa   Ruby Tiger
Phycita roborella
Phycitodes binaevella
Phyllocnistis unipunctella
Phyllonorycter
acerifoliella
Phyllonorycter
blancardella
Phyllonorycter
corylifoliella
Phyllonorycter cydoniella
Phyllonorycter dubitella
Phyllonorycter harrisella
Phyllonorycter
heegeriella
Phyllonorycter   Firethorn Leaf Miner
leucographella
Phyllonorycter
maestingella
Phyllonorycter
messaniella
Phyllonorycter
oxyacanthae
Phyllonorycter pomonella
Phyllonorycter
quercifoliella

Phyllonorycter rajella
Phyllonorycter
salicicolella
Phyllonorycter salictella
Phyllonorycter
schreberella
Phyllonorycter
stettinensis
Phyllonorycter trifasciella
Phyllonorycter tristrigella
Phyllonorycter ulicicolella
Phyllonorycter ulmifoliella
Phylloporia bistrigella
Plagodis dolabraria   Scorched Wing
Platytes alpinella
Platytes cerussella
Plemyria rubiginata   Blue-bordered Carpet
Pleuroptya ruralis   Mother of Pearl
Plusia festucae   Gold Spot
Plutella xylostella   Diamond-backed Moth
Poecilocampa populi   December Moth
Polychrysia moneta   Golden Plusia
Polyploca ridens   Frosted Green
Prays fraxinella   Ash Bud Moth
Protodeltote pygarga   Marbled White Spot
Pseudargyrotoza
conwagana
Pseudoips prasinana   Green Silver-lines
Pseudoterpna pruinata   Grass Emerald
atropunctaria
Psyche casta
Pterapherapteryx   Small Seraphim
sexalata
Pterophorus   White Plume Moth
pentadactyla
Pterostoma palpina   Pale Prominent
Ptilodon capucina   Coxcomb Prominent
Ptilodon cucullina   Maple Prominent
Ptycholoma lecheana
Ptycholomoides
aeriferanus
Pyralis farinalis   Meal Moth
Pyrrhia umbra   Bordered Sallow
Rheumaptera undulata   Scallop Shell
Rhizedra lutosa   Large Wainscot
Rhyacia simulans   Dotted Rustic

Rhyacionia pinicolana	
Rivula sericealis	Straw Dot
Rusina ferruginea	Brown Rustic
Saturnia pavonia	Emperor Moth
Schrankia costaestrigalis	Pinion-streaked Snout
Schreckensteinia festaliella	
Scoliopteryx libatrix	Herald
Scoparia ambigualis	
Scoparia pyralella	
Scoparia subfusca	
Scopula emutaria	Rosy Wave
Scopula imitaria	Small Blood-vein
Scopula marginepunctata	Mullein Wave
Scotopteryx chenopodiata	Shaded Broad-bar
Scrobipalpa instabilella	
Scrobipalpa nitentella	
Scrobipalpa salinella	
Scrobipalpa samadenisis plantaginella	
Scrobipalpa suaedella	
Scythris picaepennis	
Scythropia crataegella	Hawthorn Moth
Selenia dentaria	Early Thorn
Selenia lunularia	Lunar Thorn
Selenia tetralunaria	Purple Thorn
Semiaspilates ochrearia	Yellow Belle
Semioscopis steinkellneriana	
Sesia bembeciformis	Lunar Hornet Moth
Simyra albovenosa	Reed Dagger
Smerinthus ocellata	Eyed Hawk-moth
Sophronia semicostella	
Spaelotis ravida	Stout Dart
Spilonota ocellana	Bud Moth
Spilosoma lubricipeda	White Ermine
Spilosoma luteum	Buff Ermine
Spilosoma urticae	Water Ermine
Stenoptilia pterodactyla	
Stenoptilia zophodactylus	
Stigmella aurella	
Stigmella betulicola	
Stigmella catharticella	

Stigmella centifoliella	
Stigmella confusella	
Stigmella crataegella	
Stigmella hybnerella	
Stigmella lapponica	
Stigmella lemniscella	
Stigmella luteella	
Stigmella malella	Apple Pygmy
Stigmella obliquella	
Stigmella oxyacanthella	
Stigmella perpygmaeella	
Stigmella regiella	
Stigmella roborella	
Stigmella ruficapitella	
Stigmella sakhalinella	
Stigmella salicis	
Stigmella samiatella	
Stigmella suberivora	
Stigmella tityrella	
Stigmella trimaculella	
Stigmella ulmivora	
Swammerdamia caesiella	
Swammerdamia pyrella	
Synanthedon vespiformis	Yellow-legged Clearwing
Synaphe punctalis	
Syncopacma larseniella	
Syncopacma taeniolella	
Syndemis musculana	
Teleiopsis diffinis	
Tethea ocularis octogesimea	Figure of Eighty
Thalpophila matura	Straw Underwing
Thera britannica	Spruce Carpet
Thera obeliscata	Grey Pine Carpet
Tholera decimalis	Feathered Gothic
Thumatha senex	Round-winged Muslin
Thyatira batis	Peach Blossom
Timandra comae	Blood-vein
Tinea semifulvella	
Tinea trinotella	
Tischeria ekebladella	
Tortricodes alternella	
Tortrix viridana	Green Oak Tortrix

Trachycera advenella
Trachycera marmorea
Trifurcula immundella
Tyria jacobaeae   Cinnabar
Udea lutealis
Udea olivalis
Udea prunalis
Watsonalla binaria   Oak Hook-tip
Xanthia aurago   Barred Sallow
Xanthia gilvago   Dusky-lemon Sallow
Xanthia icteritia   Sallow
Xanthia togata   Pink-barred Sallow
Xanthorhoe ferrugata   Dark-barred Twin-spot
                             Carpet
Xanthorhoe fluctuata   Garden Carpet
Xanthorhoe montanata   Silver-ground Carpet
Xanthorhoe spadicearia   Red Twin-spot Carpet
Xestia c-nigrum   Setaceous Hebrew
                             Character
Xestia sexstrigata   Six-striped Rustic
Xestia triangulum   Double Square-spot
Xestia xanthographa   Square-spot Rustic
Xylocampa areola   Early Grey
Yponomeuta evonymella   Bird-cherry Ermine
Yponomeuta padella   Orchard Ermine
Yponomeuta rorrella   Willow Ermine
Ypsolopha dentella   Honeysuckle Moth
Ypsolopha lucella
Ypsolopha parenthesella
Ypsolopha scabrella
Ypsolopha ustella
Ypsolopha vittella
Zanclognatha   Fan-foot
tarsipennalis
Zeiraphera isertana
Zeuzera pyrina   Leopard Moth
Zygaena filipendulae   Six-spot Burnet

BUTTERFLIES

Aglais urticae   Small Tortoiseshell
Anthocharis cardamines   Orange Tip
Aphantopus hyperantus   Ringlet
Aricia agestis   Brown Argus
Callophrys rubi   Green Hairstreak

Celastrina argiolus   Holly Blue
britanna
Coenonympha   Small Heath
pamphilus
Colias croceus   Clouded Yellow
Cynthia cardui   Painted Lady
Gonepteryx rhamni   Brimstone
Inachis io   Peacock
Lasiommata megera   Wall
Lycaena phlaeas   Small Copper
Maniola jurtina   Meadow Brown
Nymphalis antiopa   Camberwell Beauty
Ochlodes venata faunus   Large Skipper
Pararge aegeria   Speckled Wood
Pieris brassicae   Large White
Pieris napi   Green-Veined White
Pieris rapae   Small White
Polygonia c-album   Comma
Polyommatus icarus   Common Blue
Pyronia tithonus   Gatekeeper
britanniae
Quercusia quercus   Purple Hairstreak
Thymelicus lineola   Essex Skipper
Thymelicus sylvestris   Small Skipper
Vanessa atalanta   Red Admiral

TRICHOPTERA   CADDIS FLIES

Adicella reducta
Agraylea multipuntata
Athripsodes atterimus
Glyphotaelius pellucidus
Holocentropus dubius
Holocentropus stagnalis
Leptocerus tineiformis
Limnephilus auricula
Limnephilus marmoratus
Limnephilus rhombicus
Mystacides longicornis
Phryganea grandis
Oecetis furva
Triaenodes bicolor

DIPTERA   FLIES

Aedes detritus
Aedes rusticus

Aedes cantans

Anopheles claviger

Anopheles maculipinis

Agromyza alnibetulae

Asphondylia sarothamni

Atylotus latistriatus

Baccha elongata

Bellardia vulgaris

Beris chalybata

Bibio marci

Bibio reticulatus

Bombylius major

Chaoborus crystallinus

Cheilosia albitarsis s.l.

Cheilosia cynocephala

Cheilosia fraterna

Cheilosia grossa

Cheilosia proxima

Cheilosia scutellata

Cheilosia urbana

Cheilosia vernalis

Chirosia betuleti

Chloromyia formosa

Chrysogaster hirtella

Chrysogaster solstitialis

Chrysopilus cristatus

Chrysops relictus

Chrysotoxum bicinctum

Coenosia testacea

Conops quadrifasciatus

Contarinia petiole

Coquillettidia richiardii

Culex territans

Culiseta morisitans

Culiseta litorea

Dasineura crataegi

Dasineura plicatrix

Dasineura urticae

Dasysyrphus albostriatus

Dasysyrphus venustus

Dilophus febrilis

Dioctria baumhaueri

Dioctria rufipes

Egle ciliata

Epicampocera succincta

Epistrophe eligans

Episyrphus balteatus

Eriothrix rufomaculata

Eristalinus aeneus

Eristalis arbustorum

Eristalis intricarius

Eristalis nemorum

Eristalis pertinax

Eristalis tenax

Eupeodes luniger

Eurithia anthophila

Graphomya maculata

Gymnocheta viridis

Haematopota bigoti

Haematopota pluvialis

Haematopota subcylindrica

Helina evecta

Helophilus hybridus

Helophilus pendulus

Hybomitra ciureai

Hydrophoria lancifera

Iteomyia capreae

Jaapiella veronicae

Leucozona lucorum

Lipara lucens

Lypha dubia

Macrodiplosis dryobia

Melangyna umbellatarum

Melanostoma scalare

Melieria crassipennis

Melieria picta

Meliscaeva auricollis

Metasyrphus latifasciatus

Musca autumnalis

Myathropa florae

Myopa testacea

Nemotelus notatus

Neoascia podagrica

Neoascia tenur

Neomyia viridescens

Neria cibaria

Odontomyia tigrina

Oplodontha viridula
Parhelophilus versicolor
Phaonia serva
Phaonia tuguriorum
Phasia hemiptera
Pherbina coryleti
Pipiza noctiluca
Pipizella varipes
Platycheirus albimanus
Platycheirus clypeatus agg.
Platycheirus manicatus
Platycheirus peltatus agg.
Poecilobothrus nobilitatus
Pollenia rudis
Pollenia vespillo
Rabdophaga salicis
Rhamphomyia sulcata
Rondaniola bursaria
Scaeva pyrastri
Setisaquamalonchaea fumosa

Sicus ferrugineus
Sphaerophoria rueppellii
Sphaerophoria scripta
Stratiomys chamaelon
Syritta pipiens
Syrphus ribesii
Syrphus vitripennis
Tabanus autumnalis
Thecophora atra
Thereva nobilitata
Tipula maxima
Trichophona immaculata
Tropidia scita
Urophora cardui
Volucella bombylans
Volucella pellucens
Wachtliella rosarum
Xanthogramma pedissequum

AMPHIBIANS

Bufo bufo

NEWTS, FROGS,TOADS

Common Toad

A rare bird far out on the salt marsh attracts a flock of telescopes.

Rana temporaria	Common Frog
Triturus cristatus	Warty Newt
Triturus vulgaris	Smooth Newt

REPTILES

SNAKES & LIZARDS

Anguis fragilis	Slow-worm
Lacerta vivipara	Viviparous Lizard
Natrix natrix	Grass Snake
Vipera berus	Adder

AVES

BIRDS

** over/on Colne Estuary or saltings   * not seen recently

Accipiter nisus	Sparrowhawk
Acrocephalus paludicola	Aquatic Warbler
Acrocephalus palustris	Marsh Warbler
Acrocephalus schoenobaenus	Sedge Warbler
Acrocephalus scirpaceus	Reed Warbler
Actitis hypoleucos	Common Sandpiper
Aegithalos caudatus	Long-Tailed Tit
Alauda arvensis	Skylark
*Alca torda***	Razorbill
Alcedo atthis	Kingfisher
Alectoris rufa	Red-Legged Partridge
*Alle alle***	Little Auk
Anas acuta	Pintail
Anas clypeata	Shoveler
Anas crecca	Teal
Anas penelope	Wigeon
Anas platyrhynchos	Mallard
Anas querquedula	Garganey
Anas sibilatrix	Chiloe Wigeon
Anas strepera	Gadwall
Anser albifrons	White-Fronted Goose
Anser anser	Greylag Goose
Anser brachyrhyncus	Pink-Footed Goose
Anser fabalis	Bean Goose
Anthus petrosus	Rock Pipit
Anthus pratensis	Meadow Pipit
Anthus trivialis	Tree Pipit
Apus apus	Swift
Ardea cinerea	Grey Heron
*Ardea purpurea***	Purple Heron
Arenaria interpres	Turnstone
Asio flammeus	Short-Eared Owl
Asio otus	Long-Eared Owl
Athene noctua	Little Owl
Aythya ferina	Pochard
Aythya fuligula	Tufted Duck
Aythya marila	Scaup
Bombycilla garrulus	Waxwing
Botaurus stellaris	Bittern
Branta bernicla	Brent Goose
Branta canadensis	Canada Goose
Branta leucopsis	Barnacle Goose
Bucephala clangula	Goldeneye
Burhinus oedicnemus	Stone-Curlew
Buteo buteo	Buzzard
Buteo lagopus	Rough-Legged Buzzard
Calidris alba	Sanderling
Calidris alpina	Dunlin
Calidris canutus	Knot
Calidris ferruginea	Curlew Sandpiper
Calidris maritima	Purple Sandpiper
Calidris minuta	Little Stint
*Caprimulgus europaeus**	Nightjar
Carduelis cannabina	Linnet
Carduelis carduelis	Goldfinch
Carduelis chloris	Greenfinch
Carduelis flammea	Redpoll
*Carduelis flavirostris**	Twite
Carduelis spinus	Siskin
Carpodacus erythrinus	Scarlet Rosefinch
Certhia familiaris	Treecreeper
Cettia cetti	Cetti's Warbler
Charadrius dubius	Little Ringed Plover
Charadrius hiaticula	Ringed Plover
*Chlidonias niger***	Black Tern
Circus aeruginosus	Marsh Harrier
Circus cyaneus	Hen Harrier
Circus pygargus	Montagu's Harrier
*Clangula hyemalis***	Long-Tailed Duck
Coccothraustes coccothraustes	Hawfinch
Columba oenas	Stock Dove
Columba palumbus	Woodpigeon
Corvus corone agg.	Carrion Crow
Corvus frugilegus	Rook

Corvus monedula	Jackdaw	*Larus ridibundus*	Black-Headed Gull
Cuculus canorus	Cuckoo	*Larus sabini***	Sabine's Gull
*Cygnus columbianus***	Bewick's Swan	*Limosa lapponica*	Bar-Tailed Godwit
*Cygnus Cygnus***	Whooper Swan	*Limosa limosa*	Black-Tailed Godwit
Cygnus olor	Mute Swan	*Locustella naevia*	Grasshopper Warbler
Delichon urbica	House Martin	*Loxia curvirostra*	Crossbill
Dendrocopos major	Great Spotted Woodpecker	*Luscinia megarhynchos*	Nightingale
		Lymnocryptes minimus	Jack Snipe
Dendrocopos minor	Lesser Spotted Woodpecker	*Melanitta fusca***	Velvet Scoter
		*Melanitta nigra***	Common Scoter
Egretta garzetta	Little Egret	*Mergus merganser***	Goosander
Emberiza citrinella	Yellowhammer	*Mergus serrator***	Red-Breasted Merganser
Emberiza schoeniclus	Reed Bunting	*Miliaria calandra*	Corn Bunting
Eremophila alpestris	Shore Lark	*Milvus migrans**	Black Kite
Erithacus rubecula	Robin	*Milvus milvus*	Red Kite
Falco columbarius	Merlin	*Motacilla alba yarrellii*	Pied Wagtail
Falco peregrinus	Peregrine	*Motacilla cinerea*	Grey Wagtail
Falco subbuteo	Hobby	*Motacilla flava flavissima*	Yellow Wagtail
Falco tinnunculus	Kestrel	*Muscicapa striata*	Spotted Flycatcher
Ficedula hypoleuca	Pied Flycatcher	*Numenius arquata*	Curlew
Fringilla coelebs	Chaffinch	*Numenius phaeopus*	Whimbrel
Fringilla montifringilla	Brambling	*Nycticorax nycticorax**	Night Heron
Fulica atra	Coot	*Oenanthe oenanthe*	Wheatear
Gallinago gallinago	Snipe	*Oriolus oriolus**	Golden Oriole
Gallinula chloropus	Moorhen	*Oxyura jamaicensis*	Ruddy Duck
Garrulus glandarius	Jay	*Pandion haliaetus*	Osprey
*Gavia arctica***	Black-Throated Diver	*Panurus biarmicus*	Bearded Tit
*Gavia immer***	Great Northern Diver	*Parus ater*	Coal Tit
*Gavia stellata***	Red-Throated Diver	*Parus caeruleus*	Blue Tit
Haematopus ostralegus	Oystercatcher	*Parus major*	Great Tit
*Himantopus himantopus***	Black-Winged Stilt	*Parus montanus**	Willow Tit
		Parus palustris	Marsh Tit
Hirundo rustica	Swallow	*Passer domesticus*	House Sparrow
*Ixobrychus minutes**	Little Bittern	*Passer montanus**	Tree Sparrow
Jynx torquilla	Wryneck	*Perdix perdix*	Grey Partridge
*Lanius collurio**	Red-Backed Shrike	*Phalacrocorax aristotelis***	Shag
Lanius excubitor	Great Grey Shrike		
Larus argentatus	Herring Gull	*Phalacrocorax carbo*	Cormorant
Larus canus	Common Gull	*Phasianus colchicus*	Pheasant
Larus fuscus	Lesser Black-Backed Gull	*Philomachus pugnax*	Ruff
		Phoenicurus ochruros	Black Redstart
*Larus glaucoides***	Iceland Gull	*Phoenicurus phoenicurus*	Redstart
Larus marinus	Great Black-Backed Gull	*Phylloscopus collybita*	Chiffchaff
*Larus melanocephalus***	Mediterranean Gull	*Phylloscopus sibilatrix**	Wood Warbler
*Larus minutes***	Little Gull		

Phylloscopus trochilus	Willow Warbler	*Tringa erythropus*	Spotted Redshank
Pica pica	Magpie	*Tringa glareola*	Wood Sandpiper
Picus viridis	Green Woodpecker	*Tringa nebularia*	Greenshank
*Platalea leucorodia***	Spoonbill	*Tringa ochropus*	Green Sandpiper
*Plectrophenax nivalis**	Snow Bunting	*Tringa tetanus*	Redshank
Pluvialis apricaria	Golden Plover	*Troglodytes troglodytes*	Wren
Pluvialis squatarola	Grey Plover	*Turdus iliacus*	Redwing
*Podiceps auritus***	Slavonian Grebe	*Turdus merula*	Blackbird
Podiceps cristatus	Great Crested Grebe	*Turdus philomelos*	Song Thrush
*Podiceps grisegena***	Red-Necked Grebe	*Turdus pilaris*	Fieldfare
*Podiceps nigricollis***	Black-Necked Grebe	*Turdus torquatus*	Ring Ouzel
*Porzana porzana**	Spotted Crake	*Turdus viscivorus*	Mistle Thrush
Prunella modularis	Dunnock	*Tyto alba*	Barn Owl
*Puffinus puffinus***	Manx Shearwater	*Uria aalge***	Guillemot
Pyrrhula pyrrhula	Bullfinch	*Vanellus vanellus*	Lapwing
Rallus aquaticus	Water Rail		
Recurvirostra avosetta	Avocet	**MAMMALIA**	**MAMMALS**
Regulus ignicapillus	Firecrest	Apodemus flavicollis	Yellow-Necked Mouse
Regulus regulus	Goldcrest	Apodemus sylvaticus	Wood Mouse
Riparia riparia	Sand Martin	Arvicola terrestris	Water Vole
*Rissa tridactyla***	Kittiwake	Clethrionomys glareolus	Bank Vole
Saxicola rubetra	Whinchat	Erinaceus europaeus	Hedgehog
Saxicola torquata	Stonechat	Lepus capensis	Brown Hare
Scolopax rusticola	Woodcock	Meles meles	Badger
Sitta europaea	Nuthatch	Micromys minutus	Harvest Mouse
*Somateria mollissima***	Eider	Microtus agrestis	Field Vole
*Stercorarius parasiticus***	Arctic Skua	Muntiacus reevesi	Muntjac
Sterna albifrons	Little Tern	Mus musculus	House Mouse
Sterna caspia	Caspian Tern	Mustela erminea	Stoat
Sterna hirundo	Common Tern	Mustela nivalis	Weasel
*Sterna paradisaea***	Arctic Tern	Neomys fodiens	Water Shrew
*Sterna sandvicensis***	Sandwich Tern	Oryctolagus cuniculus	Rabbit
Streptopelia decaocto	Collared Dove	Phoca vitulina	Common Seal
Streptopelia turtur	Turtle Dove	Pipistrellus pipistrellus	Pipistrelle
Strix aluco	Tawny Owl	Plecotus auritus	Brown Long-Eared Bat
Sturnus vulgaris	Starling	Rattus norvegicus	Brown Rat
Sylvia atricapilla	Blackcap	Sciurus carolinensis	Grey Squirrel
Sylvia borin	Garden Warbler	Sorex araneus	Common Shrew
*Sylvia cantillans**	Subalpine Warbler	Sorex minutus	Pygmy Shrew
Sylvia communis	Whitethroat	Talpa europaea	Mole
Sylvia curruca	Lesser Whitethroat	Vulpes vulpes	Fox
*Sylvia nisoria***	Barred Warbler		
Tachybaptus ruficollis	Little Grebe		
Tadorna tadorna	Shelduck